THE GENTLE SLEEP SOLUTION

The naturally nurturing way to help your baby sleep

Chireal Shallow

LONDON

1 3 5 7 9 10 8 6 4 2

Vermilion, an imprint of Ebury Publishing,
20 Vauxhall Bridge Road,
London SW1V 2SA

Vermilion is part of the Penguin Random House group of companies whose
addresses can be found at global.penguinrandomhouse.com

Penguin
Random House
UK

Permission to use 'Thinking Styles' on page 82 has been kindly
granted by the CCI, Centre for Clinical Interventions

'The Valued Living Questionnaire' on page 113 has been reproduced
from *Mindfulness for Two* (Wilson and DuFrene, 2007) with kind permission of
New Harbinger Publications. All rights reserved

First published by Vermilion in 2015

www.eburypublishing.co.uk

A CIP catalogue record for this book is available from the British Library

ISBN 9781785040016

Printed and bound in Great Britain by Clays Ltd, St Ives PLC

Penguin Random House is committed to a sustainable
future for our business, our readers and our planet.
This book is made from Forest Stewardship Council®
certified paper.

The author has chosen to use a combination of 'she' and 'her' and 'he' and 'him'; this is not to say that any part is relevant only to one sex, or that the sexes are interchangeable. It is a positive move towards balance and equality.

Contents

Acknowledgements

FIRSTLY, THIS BOOK WOULD NOT BE HERE IF IT WEREN'T FOR MY daughters Pariss, Suraha, Sophie and Charlotte. Not only were you my inspiration, but you were the catalysts that allowed me to go on to help thousands of other children and their parents. I want to say a big thank you for allowing me to use you as my guinea pigs and for being such gracious, willing and fast learning students. You have allowed me to learn more about myself in the process or helping you all to sleep. I am truly honored to be your mum. I look forward to watching you grow into amazingly loving caring women with children of your own who sleep well too.

To all the amazing families I have worked with over the last 11 years, who came to me in times of need, trusted me and allowed me into their homes and we worked hard together to reach your goals. Thank-you for allowing me the opportunity to share your successes and your friendship.

I owe extreme gratitude to the people that have helped me on this journey, not only these recent months but through out the years when writing this book was just an aspiration. My mum Victoria without a doubt is a special person who has been my biggest fan, second only to my little sisters Abigail and Emily. The unwavering support from my extended family their grounding has been invaluable.

I want to thank those who at the very start of me setting up my sleep consultancy business supported me and believed in me and kept me going, this shout out goes to you. I also thank Andrew Palmer whose daily support and friendship and encouragement will never be forgotten.

I also want to thank Samantha Jackson and Julia, my editors form Ebury who believed in this project and came to me with this idea of putting my work together into a format that could be shared with the public. I would also like to thank Justine Taylor from Ebury who heard my voice and helped me navigate and structure my work, and to my agent Diane Banks and all her staff for your expertise and reassurance.

Lastly, I want to say a special heartfelt thank you to Pariss and her friend Brodie who were keen to use their English degree skills at the very start to help shape the proposal part of this very special piece of work. You guys are awesome.

Introduction

YOUR BABY'S NOT SLEEPING AND IT'S NOT YOUR FAULT. I CAN almost hear you gasp. That's right – it's not your fault and it most certainly is not your child's fault. Your baby is doing what she is designed to do – responding to her environment. You are doing all you can to get through the day (to stay alive, to stay on top of things), and you are doing the best you can in the moment. I will not judge you, place blame or discourage you. I am tired of the advice that blames parents or the child for poor sleeping habits, so I can only imagine how it must make you feel. As a single mother of four children, I am well aware of the pressure from well-meaning health-care professionals, families and friends. Their advice and support is undoubtedly coming from a place of love and yet all this wealth of advice turns into pressure and you experience pressure, pressure to please, pressure to do the right thing, pressure to not disappoint, pressure to listen and pressure to be the best parent you can be. When I look back to when my babies were young I needed a helping hand not a wagging finger and I am guessing you do too. You have already taken the first step – now let me guide you towards sleeping success.

The study of children's sleep is imbalanced in favour of research into adult sleep difficulties, ignoring the fact that childhood sleeping problems, of which there is a varying array of issues, are extremely common, and may be the origin of some sleep problems found in adulthood. There is a lot that is not understood about sleep disorders in general, and many long-suffering families do not come to the attention of clinicians due to the widespread belief that disordered sleep is not a real problem, or that it's a problem to be endured. Conversely, there is a sufficient amount of important information that we do know about sleep as well as sleep problems that relate to children that need to be shared. The issue of how sleep in children affects cognitive functioning, mood and behaviour has been observed and it has been accepted by those in the profession that many childhood sleep issues can be managed using psychological behavioural techniques. Moreover, what this says is that rather than seeing the problem as one to visit your GP or health visitor with using their medical or pharmacological approach, you are more likely to be successful using a behavioural approach and as such this is where psychologists such as myself have much to contribute to deeper understanding of how to effectively overcome childhood sleep issues.

Who I am

I am a consultant psychologist, HCPC registered and BABCP accredited psychotherapist and sleep expert working with adults, families and children. Over my many years of practice I have specialised in anxiety disorders and depression, post-traumatic stress disorder (PTSD), childhood trauma and sleep difficulties.

I have over 15 years of experience within the NHS and private sector, and I have helped thousands of individuals and families with emotional, behavioural and/or occupational difficulties. I am able to provide insight in understanding the issues that cause people to struggle in their home, social life and within the workplace. I have enjoyed using my interpersonal skills and therapeutic talents to enable people to begin their journey of personal change. Not only as an excellent motivational coach, but also as an intuitive and integrative psychotherapist, I am able to help all my clients achieve and often exceed their desired goals and improve their feelings of self-worth. I strongly and firmly believe that a warm and non-judgemental approach allows my clients to form strong therapeutic relational bonds that will effect change, and creates a space for my clients to benefit from an opportunity to achieve optimal personal growth.

My training both academically and practically included models of psychopathology, clinical psychometrics and neuro-psychology. I have been specifically trained in distinct psychological therapies, CBT, systemic family therapy, solution-focused therapy, mindfulness, and compassion-focused therapy, functional analysis and dialectical behavioural therapy, including lifespan developmental psychology. My commitment to providing clinical excellence, personal and professional development means that I maintain an on-going portfolio of clinical hours, supervision and attendance of CPD training courses and events. Having studied at the University of Surrey, East London University and gained a CBT qualification at Royal Holloway UCL, I have benefitted from being taught by some of the most prominent and influential psychologists in the field of anxiety, depression and trauma.

I have helped individuals, families and children with relationship breakdown, separation and attachment issues, divorce, family issues, communication problems, anger management, bereavement, parenting issues, children's sleeping problems and adult insomnia, stress and anxiety, depression, low self-esteem, lack of confidence, eating disorders, obsessive-compulsive disorder (OCD), post-traumatic, specific phobias, panic issues, work difficulties, childhood trauma and self-harm. Sleep features heavily in all of the problems I have worked with and thus this makes me extremely qualified to be coaching you and your family through your current sleep difficulties.

How this book will work for you

You can use *The Gentle Sleep Solution* in a number of ways. If you really are at a loss and do not know where to start then it may be helpful for you to read this book from cover to cover, so that you can understand the principles and practise all the skills, that will be of most benefit to you, and then formulate a plan. If you are a parent who has an idea of where you are and what you might need to do, then you can dip in and out of this book and use it as a gentle guide. However you decide to use this book, I will coach you in how sleep disturbances affect your mood, your body, your thoughts and your actions.

I believe that the best way to make change happen when it comes to sleep is to work out what works best for you, and then do it. This means that I will not set any rigid rules but offer new ways of thinking and acting. If one approach works, then great! But if another doesn't work for you and your family, don't despair. A trick your friend used to get her baby to sleep may not work for you, and there's nothing wrong with that. All it means was that 'trick' worked for that particular baby, in that particular family under a particular set of conditions. I will help you to pick the right tools that work for your family and applying them in a way that minimises distress and discomfort for you and your baby. At times, some of my advice may fly in the face of what you have heard from other sources, but I guarantee you that the principles work, and they work because they are grounded in evidence and have been tested and verified to work. In addition, my advice, such as my view on routines and how you use Tracy Hogg's PU/PD method, is designed in such a way that you can pick and choose which elements work best for you, so you are able to make a sleep plan that is flexible and meets your needs.

This book is different from others on the market because we use evidence-based psychological methods in a way that has never been used before to help coach parents with their children's sleep. I will show you how to use CBT, or cognitive behavioural therapy, to develop skills to overcome your sleep issue, and give you attachment tools and mindfulness techniques to change how you respond to certain issues and to manage your emotions. I will also show you CBT techniques to promote healthy sleeping patterns in your child.

The CBT model focuses on gaining a good sound understanding of your problem, identifying vicious cycles where your thinking and behaviour keeps you trapped, and using CBT techniques to make meaningful and long-lasting change, where we focus on challenging how we think and adapting our behaviour so that we can form compassionate cycles.

My advice will change the way you look at and feel about sleep for ever. Not only will you feel more confident, you will be empowered with the truth about sleep, which will dissolve away your fears. You will no longer feel dread before bedtime and your bedtime battles will be no more. I am going to guide, coach and support you through each stage towards establishing a better sleeping habit for you and your child.

Throughout this book you'll find boxes that contain stand-out tips, and what I call 'golden keys', both of which will give you advice and ideas on how to get your baby into a compassionate cycle of sleep. Always remember: the best and the brightest golden key is you, and with the tools I give you, you will find the best way of getting your child into a sleep pattern that works for all members of your family.

I make no apologies – this is a sleep book – but it's a different kind of sleep-training book designed for babies aged from zero to two years of age. It will help you get your child to sleep, but what it won't do is waste your time, patronise you or tell you all the things you might be doing wrong. That's not my style – blame is unhelpful at best and damaging at worst. My book is written with real families with real issues in mind. If you're a single parent, a family with more than one child, a parent with twins, a parent with children with special needs, a family that needs to travel, blended families of all kinds... this book is for you. This book is not about putting your life on hold while you train your baby to sleep, it's about getting your child to sleep while life happens and how to continue with your life while maintaining a natural sleep pattern though nurturing.

When I say this is a book for real families, I can stand behind this statement with conviction because I did it, and if I can, I have every belief that you can too, with a little support from this book. I was a single mother of four girls and raising two-week-old twins by myself. I had school runs and after-school activities and took holidays abroad. I got my twin girls sleeping through the night at four months. They are now 11 years old and we haven't ever looked back.

Chireal's Tip Bits

To be successful on this plan you will need an open mind – and a pencil and notepad.

The issue, as I saw it when I was pregnant with the twins, was that there was one main way of getting your child to sleep: 'cry it out'. As a parent I was not keen on this method of sleep training and as a psychologist I questioned why there should be only one method. What happened to choice? What if I wanted to try something else? I decided to see what else was out there that could help me and my family with the sleep issues we were facing. I soon found that there was not very much out there that specifically related to twins. Perhaps I was looking in the wrong places. Yes, there were some helpful suggestions that appealed to my style of parenting, such as those from the baby whisperer, Dr Williams Sears, but that did not feel like a complete solution for me as I had only one pair of arms, four children to look after and two babies who might choose to cry at the same time. I needed a complete structured plan to help me in my unique situation that I had not found in books, parenting sites or sleep forums. The answer, as I soon began to realise, lay in the methods I had used in my clinical practice to effect behavioural change in my clients. My task was to translate that to sleep, which after all is just another form of behaviour.

I am a fan of routines, routines that work for the family, that is. I am a believer that routines are helpful and have a place in helping to establish a sleep routine. Where this book differs from others in this subject is how you construct your routine, which I talk more about in later chapters. But routines are not the panacea to sleep problems. Routines are part of the process and should be viewed and managed as such. Having a routine is very much like having a road map but you need to use the direction and the signpost together in order to work out how to reach your destination.

So with two hats on – the psychologist's and mother's – I set about devising a plan based on CBT, attachment tools and mindfulness on trying to shape my behaviour and that of my children. First I thought about what it was I wanted to do. This might seem crazy, because the simple answer was I wanted both my babies to sleep. However, before that could be achieved I needed to think about the reasons why my children found it difficult to sleep – that is, what were the underlying factors preventing my children from sleeping well. In small children there are many reasons why long sleeping hours may be difficult to achieve – needing to feed frequently and having an immature body rhythm are major sleep barriers in newborns. So the logical initial step was for me to think about what was realistic. Realistically, how long can I expect my newborn twins to sleep for? Once I set my goal and accepted that sleeping through the night for a newborn consisted of five hours in the first few weeks, I decided that I would not beat myself up or feel like a bad mother because Mrs Jones down the road had a newborn sleeping 28 hours a day. I knew my goal was realistic and easy to achieve and that things would improve.

The second step was to think about what factors I was in control of and what I was not in control of. This meant looking at my own behaviour. Could there be things that I was thinking or doing that were a barrier to my children sleeping? This relates to how CBT can help as I was asking questions that related to my perception of my problem, how that made me feel and what thoughts I had about me, my situation and my ability to solve the issues. I asked myself, what things in the home am I in control of that could make their sleep better? This has been referred to in some texts – namely Tracy Hogg's *Baby Whisperer* books – as 'accidental parenting'. I didn't want my fears about being a single parent to newborn twins and two older children to affect my mood so much that I became demotivated at best or depressed at worst. I also wanted to try and avoid rocking my babies to sleep, or feeding to sleep, as I was well aware of the problems that can arise if this type of accidental parenting occurs. What I began to realise was that the biggest potential barrier to my babies sleeping was my anxiety at not being able to manage the overwhelming sense of loneliness, and the fear of coping with my twins on my own. I needed to find a plan that worked with me to help me with my negative thoughts and strong emotions. For me, mindfulness was the single most helpful thing in breaking down the barrier to establishing natural sleep patterns for my babies in a nurturing way. Mindfulness meant that I took one moment at a time, focused on one thing at a time, relaxed and avoided thoughts that would, if I allowed them, trigger strong negative emotions and kickstart my vicious cycles. I didn't want to get caught up in a vicious cycle; I wanted a cycle that would lead me to establish a natural sleep pattern in my children. I also wanted to feel helpful, in control and calm, and I identified what measures I already had in place that were clear examples of good, planned parenting.

Step three entailed learning how to communicate with my babies. I needed to understand their language and meet their needs in a systematic way, then soothing them to be in a calm state so that they were in the perfect position for sleep. As newborns their main language was crying, so I had to listen to their sounds and work out what they were trying to communicate to me. I also used their body language as a guide in the first instance. I have included a chart on page 42–43 to help you learn your child's crying language.

Step four involved putting my plan into action over a period of four weeks. I was dedicated and consistent and when my babies were four months old they were sleeping through the night. Though my babies were waking for feeds throughout the night, I did not count these as wakes as these were essential to meeting their needs and outside my control. My babies would wake in the night, babble, and then go back off to sleep without needing to be soothed by me. I also did not count this as wakes as they were demonstrating their ability to self-soothe, which I wanted to encourage. When we look at sleep patterns in more detail you will see that babies are designed to wake up several times in the night; in fact, heavy sleeping in a child is a cause for concern. The issue is not whether your child wakes in the night, but more that she is unable to move to the next phase of the sleep cycle without a parent offering comfort, a feed or meeting some other critical need. This issue for most parents, particularly mothers, is that they are often woken by their babies stirring and so they will count these as 'wakes', not as a result of their babies' natural sleep pattern. This increases the perception of the sleep problem and further serves to frustrate the parents. This is where CBT principles comes into play as it challenges the thoughts and perceptions of parents and enables them to view and experience their problem in a different way. Seeing the problem in a different way typically takes the heat out of it, and reduces its effect on parents so the problem doesn't feel so bad.

My gentle sleep system using CBT, mindfulness and attachment tools will help you assess the underlying reason your child is not sleeping.

The first stage demonstrates how you can assess what your sleep problem is – whether it is anxiety or dependency or a mixture of both – and identifying your unhelpful thinking styles.

The second stage shows you new ways to communicate and respond to your child. By matching the level of parental responsiveness to the level of your child's distress you will be able to reduce your child's anxiety and dependency. This also will allow your baby to fall asleep independently and with ease. In addition, I will show you how to use mindfulness to manage your emotions and challenge you own unhelpful thinking.

The third stage will coach you on how to devise and implement your plan based on your parenting style, your child's temperament and through reading your child's language.

Now that you have the tools for establishing and maintaining healthy sleep patterns, you will use the fourth stage to begin recording and monitoring your progress – see the appendices at the back of this book. During this stage you will work on maintenance and troubling shooting for long-term success.

If this feels unfeasible to you, please don't be disheartened: remember what I said about setting realistic and achievable goals. In a few short steps I will guide you through my plan of achieving natural sleeping patterns for your family. After all, you deserve it.

By reading this book you are already on your journey towards change and I will guide you through the common myths that surround sleep. I will provide you with a sound and coherent understanding of how your baby developed her sleep problems and how you can turn things around. I will give you the confidence to tackle these problems head-on and will empower you to make the essential behavioural changes that will significantly affect the quality of your sleep. I will show you some of the common accidental thinking and behaviour styles that maintain your baby's sleep problem and teach you how to avoid some of the common pitfalls that are associated with poor sleeping habits. In addition, you will learn how modern technology, your perceptions and your behaviours affect your sleep and how you can balance these competing obligations to enhance your sleep. I will talk you through why some methods work for you and why others don't, which will enable you to make an informed choice on how to build your own unique sleep plan. I will teach you how to respond to your baby by matching your reassurance to the level of their distress and behavioural change techniques so that you will become your own sleep expert and gain mastery and control over your baby's daily sleeping pattern.

By using my techniques not only will you achieve a natural sleeping pattern, you will be able to do the very things that have been evading you all this time… maintenance and sustainability all by just nurturing your family naturally. You will learn how to measure your progress and keep on track even when something happens that upsets your routine. Ultimately, by consolidating all the lessons and skills within my sleep system, I will teach you how to sleep.

Chapter 1

Understanding sleep

Did you know: Vincent Van Gogh was unable to sleep for three weeks and the effects of his insomnia have been expressed in some of his art work?

WHEN AS A NEW MOTHER I WAS LOOKING FOR SLEEP ADVICE ON the Internet and in books I discovered that there is a huge disparity between the amount of research into children's sleep habits and that of adults. Sleep in itself was a poor relation when it came to in-depth study, and children's sleep was even worse. The problem lay in the commonality of sleep issues in childhood and the view that having sleep problems was a rite of passage for a new parent. The medical view was that there were far more serious conditions worthy of research grants. However, sleep problems and sleep disorders can be very damaging for the individuals affected and disruptive for their family. And just because a problem is common does not mean that it's not a problem with huge negative implications if left unaddressed – we know that without sleep we are unable to function, grow and thrive. So learning how to gain good sleep is vital. Research suggests that 22 per cent of nine-month-olds have difficulty settling to sleep, as do 15 to 20 per cent of one- to two-year-olds. Frequent night waking is a problem for 42 per cent of nine-month-olds and 20 to 26 per cent of one- to two-year-olds. After six months, new sleep problems may emerge and night waking happens in 50 per cent of children who had previously slept through the night. That said, most sleep problems in children are temporary and do not have long-lasting side effects. However, during the period that parents have to endure sleep deprivation, the devastation it can have on health and relationships is significant. I believe that parents do not have to accept childhood sleep habits as a phase they should endure but one they can enjoy, manage and master.

Keep a sleep log; have one week of your baby's sleep pattern prior to starting the plan.

Basic sleep facts

Sleep is a basic human function, and while there are many different theories on the function of sleep, one thing is clear and all the theories agree upon: we all need sleep. Sleep can be described as an active state that is crucial to the quality of our lives and our well-being; during this time the body is able to repair and build proteins and hormones essential for us to use during the day. However basic, sleep is an inherently complex process. How much sleep we need and the pattern of that sleep varies from person to person and changes throughout our lives. Typical environments for sleep to occur are quite dark conditions, where the body is limited to movement and usually in a lying down position. During sleep we pass through two distinct states: non-rapid-eye-movement sleep and rapid-eye-movement sleep (REM).

I hope that you can see that your child's sleep, or lack of it, is not your fault. It would make sense that something this intricate, subtle and adaptive would be hard to achieve in oneself let alone in another human being.

In order to understand the complexity of children's sleep it is probably best to begin with examining adult sleep cycles. First, it is important to understand the stages of sleep. These stages are organised in a series of cycles, with each cycle lasting 90 minutes that repeats through the course of the night. So let's start at the beginning, from when your head touches the pillow and you close your eyes.

* Stage 1 is what we call the transition phase – the space between wakefulness and sleep. This typically lasts only a matter of minutes before progressing to the second stage.
* Stage 2 sleep makes up 50–60 per cent of adult sleep. The first phase in this part of the cycle is generally short and we experience the deepest part of our sleep during the first third of the night.
* Stage 3 is part of deep sleep and acts as the transitional element. Deep, slow brainwaves known as delta waves begin to emerge during this part of the sleep phase where we move from light sleep to very deep sleep.
* Stage 4 makes up deep sleep. During stage 4 the brain activity settles into a harmonised rhythm. We can refer to stages 1, 2, 3 and 4 as non-REM sleep.
* Stage 5 is known as REM sleep – a form of light sleep where our body is still while our eyes are moving, and this stage of sleep is where our dreams are formed. Our bodies become paralysed and our brain increases in activity.

Chireal's Tip Bits

Focus on what you want, not on what other parents are doing.

So, how does this cycle work? Our circadian body rhythm is regulated by internal and external factors: internal factors, such as hormones produced by our body and what we eat, help to promote sleep, while external factors, such as light and dark and alarm clocks, help to regulate how and when we sleep and wake up.

Primarily, the body's rhythm is regulated by exposure to light and dark; this means that we tend to feel more tired when it is dark as opposed to when it is light. The good news for those who have problems sleeping is that the body clock can be set and reset. The body clock is flexible and adaptive, which means it is subject to change and manipulation. This puts us in a very good position as with knowledge we have the capacity to improve our sleep. In the following chapters we will look at what the barriers are to gaining that all-important desirable sleeping pattern.

How does my child sleep?

We are all born with an immature body rhythm. Simply put, your baby's pattern of sleep has not yet been organised into the conventional stages of sleep described above. This means that your newborn is not ready or equipped to sleep 'through the night'. Your baby is ready and waiting for you to help set her sleeping patterns. This means that you can use this knowledge to your advantage; you can also let yourself off the hook when your baby's pattern is so different to yours because it's not your fault.

Your baby needs a lot of care when she's awake and you may feel relieved when she drops off to sleep and looks so contented. You may worry if your baby seems to sleep less than you expect, but you'll soon be swapping stories with other parents about broken nights and tough days. The trouble is, your baby has her own sleep pattern and this can vary from day to day and night to night. In the early weeks your baby's sleep, or lack of it, will be affecting you. It's normal to feel tired as broken sleep and night feeds interrupt your previous well-adapted routine.

Remember, sleep needs and patterns vary from child to child. Newborns usually sleep about eight hours at night, but not in one long unbroken sleep; they may sleep for just one hour, or perhaps for three or five hours before waking. Expect wide variations. Some babies manage five- or six-hour stretches of sleep at night by three to four months, but many do not, and others may even be more wakeful than when they were younger.

> Because body rhythm matures with age it's probably best to focus on learning your child's cues and putting her down when she is sleepy before you try to get her set into a sleep routine. Be led by your baby's needs – gradually she will learn the difference between night and day.

The contrast between being safely wrapped up in the womb and then being born is a huge one and as new parents we are tasked with the job of helping our newborn adjust to their new world. Dr Harvey Karp calls the period straight after birth 'the fourth trimester', and maintains that human babies are born because they get too big for the womb, not because they are ready. Therefore the care we give our babies in the first few weeks is crucial in their transition from womb to outside world but the idea of the fourth trimester is also helpful to us as we now understand that our newborn needs maximum comfort, which includes sleeping on our chest, skin-to-skin contact, the security of the swaddle, and the gentle sway of being rocked. The fourth trimester is about you and your baby getting to know each other. The art is to ease your baby into the world by minimising the difference between their internal world of the womb and the external world outside of their mothers. Knowing how to respond to your baby in the first few weeks will empower you to dance to the beat of your own drum. There are no rules: accept what your baby needs to become part of this new world through guidance, comfort and love that you can provide calmly and knowingly.

Babies have different sleep patterns to adults. Adults spend 75 to 80 per cent in deep sleep and 20 to 25 per cent in shallow sleep. Babies spend 50 per cent of their time in shallow sleep and there is very good reason – our babies are by their biological nature light sleepers. You may not think it but babies' sleep cycles are essentially longer in total hours of sleep time – these calculations are based on the totality of sleep in any 24-hour period, not just at night when their sleeping habits most affect us. Babies spend a greater time in light sleep in comparison to adults and these light sleep phases last for a lot longer. All babies are light sleepers, and though both internal and external factors can contribute to help regulate and set our babies' sleeping patterns, how you respond to their needs and shape their environment and expectations will be your biggest weapon when combating the war on sleep problems.

Sleep through the ages

We know that sleep cycles change over the course of our lifetime, with young adults needing between seven and nine hours' sleep during the night and the elderly requiring between seven and eight. The biggest changes in our sleep occur during our childhood. Most sleeping patterns begin to regulate when a child is between six and nine months of age. This means that until then you can expect your baby's sleep habits to be without pattern and with frequent changes. Very new research has widened the time window that a baby sleeps for during the day. You'll see that I've put both the new time window, and the old time window as many books still follow the older research.

For the first six months of life your baby will be engaged in active sleep and will sleep on average 16–18 hours in any 24-hour period. This will reduce over time, along with the levels of sleep hormones being produced. Any sleep taken in the day is deducted from the night, so if your child sleeps more in the day, expect her to sleep less at night and vice versa. By the time your child is three years old, most of their 12–14 hours' sleep will be at night. As a guide your one-year-old should be getting 15 hours, which includes her daytime nap. Most children from the age of five until they reach puberty are sleeping soundly through the night. That said, we shall not be waiting five years before you and your family can sleep well.

- Newborns (0–3 months): New research has widened their sleep range to 14 to 17 hours a day – previous research suggested it was 12 to 18
- Infants (4–11 months): Sleep range widened two hours to 12 to 15 hours – previously it was 14 to 15
- Toddlers (1–2 years): Sleep range widened by one hour to 11 to 14 hours – previously it was 12 to 14
- Pre-schoolers (3–5): Sleep range widened by one hour to 10 to 13 hours – previously it was 11 to 13
- School-age children (6–13): Sleep range widened by one hour to 9 to 11 hours – previously it was 10 to 11
- Teenagers (14–17): Sleep range widened by one hour to 8 to 10 hours – previously it was 8.5 to 9.5
- Young adults (18–25): Sleep range is 7 to 9 hours – new age category

* Adults (26–64): Sleep range did not change and remains 7 to 9 hours
* Older adults (65+): Sleep range is 7 to 8 hours – new age category

Study results from the NSF (National Sleep Foundation)

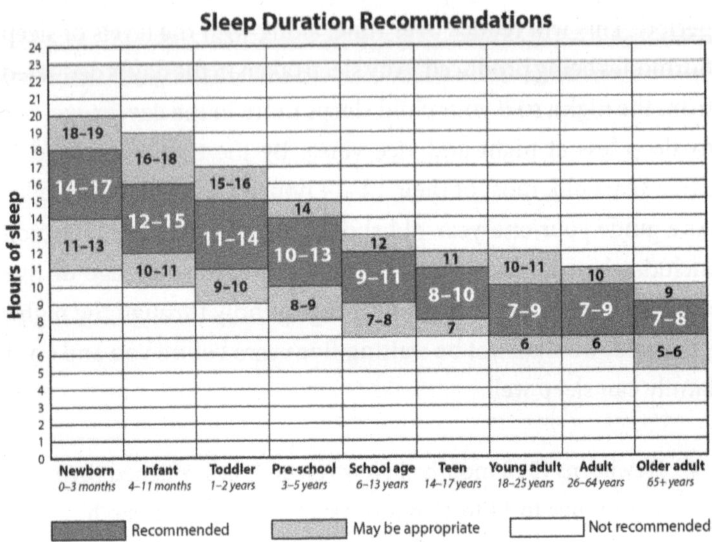

Busting common sleep myths

Popular parenting books, in my view and experience, tend to use pop psychology to support their methods and instruct you to throw your dummies away and end breastfeeding before you are ready. There is a war on sleep props, they are apparently the root of all evil and with them sleep will evade you. You are urged to eradicate these demonised things and sleep will be yours. I get so cross at these so-called 'helpful' textbooks as I work with more and more parents who are saddened by the end of breastfeeding and co-sleeping but felt they had no other choice. What if you love breastfeeding? What if your child loves their comforter? Can I tell you something amazing, something I think no one has told you before? What you have been sold is a myth, you *can* breastfeed and co-sleep and still have your baby sleep through the night. I am here to tell you that those books are wrong.

Here is an amazing illuminating fact: it's not what you do or give your child, it's how you do it. It's the function of the behaviour that is key. Allow me to bust the myths and elaborate.

MYTH: If you use associations, you will become dependent on them

It is my belief that all associations are good. Associations, as defined within the field of psychology, are generally referred to as any learned, functional connection between two or more elements. This could relate to ideas, stimuli and response, memories and it specifies the process that underlies their connection to what will happen, what will be learnt or achieved when the associate is used. So in relation to your baby's sleep, an association may look like all the elements you include in bedtime routine, such as the story, the feed, the idea and concept that at a certain time your baby should sleep. The goal – or what is to be achieved and learnt – is your baby sleeping naturally when these things are shown or presented.

There are many types of associations. Associations can be direct, controlled, induced or immediate. During the sleep process you, as a parent, will use all these types of associations as part of establishing your baby's natural sleep pattern. Associations such as dimming the lights and having a bath all signpost bedtime and communicate sleep to your child in a controlled and immediate way. Singing a bedtime song to your baby is another useful example of an induced association. Used over time and repeatedly your baby will learn that closing the curtains (a direct association) and you singing is related to her being calm and falling sleep.

One very powerful way babies can learn is through communication, both verbal and non-verbal. Verbal communicate is how we use our language and sounds to communicate with each other. Non-verbal communicate describes all ways in which we communicate without the use of spoken languages, this will include our posture, body positions, facial expressions. With the effective and proper use of associations through communicating with your baby, they will learn to make the necessary connections that lead all the way to the bedroom and towards a natural sleep pattern. Using these types of communication will form associations that will help your baby sleep and this will become an essential part of your plan.

Chireal's Tip Bits

Use associations to your advantage: they are one of the golden keys to good sleep.

MYTH: Props and cues get in the way of good-quality sleep

We all need a little help to get us off to sleep – whether it's as simple as sleeping with the window open or being on the right side of the bed, this all helps us get in the mood for sleep. I call this having your own idiosyncratic style of drifting off to sleep. Well, babies are no different, yet so-called 'experts' refer to their idiosyncrasies as 'sleep props' and 'sleep cues'. These are the things your child needs to fall asleep. In the first instance that prop could be you, but could also include all those cues and props in your bedtime routine: milk, dummy, comforter, blankets, stories, etc.... The list goes on. What's important to understand here is that there is nothing wrong with your baby having a sleep prop or cue, so long as it is independent from yourself. Your child needs signs to help her know it's time to go to sleep and she needs a little nudge in the right direction with props to offer comfort and help her feel safe when you are no longer present (as long as those props are safe and age appropriate). For this reason and this reason alone sleep props and cues can be good for your baby and very helpful to you in establishing a natural sleep pattern for your child. If these cues or props are continually used, over time your child may develop a dependency on them, but this can also be helpful in maintaining a natural sleep pattern, ensuring that your child feels safe and secure. This may be the first time you've heard someone explain sleep props in this way and it may come as a shock to you that they are no longer your enemy or things to be feared. Rather, we can use props and cues to our advantage and help our little darlings sleep well at night. Props used at bedtime can aid building a natural sleep pattern, as your baby will see this and associate your communication and their actions with sleep.

Some parents worry that over time a child may become dependent on a prop used to create a bedtime association. This needn't be a concern as by understanding the importance of associations and helping your baby to use props independently you will avoid dependency being an issue. So for example teaching your 10-month-old baby to put her dummy back in by herself is an effective use of a prop and does not create dependency on you. The association / cue and or prop should be something that is managed independent of your actions so, for example, props such as your hand or your child stroking your hair are not helpful or effective associations. These props will lead to your baby needing you each and every wake which means you are trapped, as you have now become part of the sleep routine. Therefore, for success it is important that you use props, cues and associations that are sustainable and manageable throughout the bedtime routine and throughout the night. Props, cues and associations that you can manage whether you are at home, overseas or visiting family or friends. These props could include music, pictures of you, and white noise machines.

However, when a prop becomes a dependency then we have a problem. Let me explain this with an example. If your baby falls asleep on the breast or bottle and then sleeps well through the night then this is not a problem. Your child is falling asleep with you and the breast as a prop, it does not interfere with her sleep and it works! Well done to you. On the other hand, if your baby falls asleep on the breast or bottle and wakes frequently in the night and can only get back to sleep by having milk or sucking, then your baby is dependent on this and this is something we need to address. Having a dependency is when your child requires you or your actions in order to move her to the next phase of the sleep cycle. So our job as parents is to tackle the dependencies our child may have on us and help her self-soothe, Self-soothing is another way to refer to babies being dependent on themselves – independent of us and dependent instead on their surroundings, sleep cues and props if they require or desire them. Having a prop that your child can manage herself is a good thing and can aid sleep.

Chireal's Tip Bits

When people give you advice, focus on your unique family and pick the sense from the non-sense.

MYTH: Babies can't self-soothe

Babies are born with reflexes to soothe themselves, such as the sucking reflex, the hand-to-mouth reflex, as well as moving position and paying attention to sounds and faces. The hand-to-mouth reflex in your newborn can be triggered just by stroking her cheek. The act of your stroking your baby's face causes her to begin 'rooting'; this will involve her bringing her hand to her mouth and she will automatically begin to suck. Sometimes parents confuse this action from their newborn as a sign or communication for hunger, when in fact your baby is engaging in self-soothing. Your baby sucking on her fingers provides her with huge amounts of comfort. This reflex will fade around three months, but by this time your baby has skilfully managed to gain control over her own movement and her sucking and/or self-soothing will be more intentional. Once she realises she has mastered this skill she may begin to enjoy this form of comfort. You may confuse this action with the onset of teething, but in fact your baby has learnt to self-soothe first by instinct and reflex and then second through learned behaviour and intent.

To help your baby establish a natural sleep pattern you should encourage her to self-soothe. Therefore your baby should be given the opportunity and encouragement to soothe herself, but when she is unable to, you should step in and comfort her. During soothing our babies, we often feel good and the cuddles we get from our babies can feel rewarding. If we have a baby that is not responsive to cuddles we may feel that we may have failed in some way or are not doing the right thing. However, all babies are different, and all it means is that your baby has a temperament that requires you to find another soothing technique. Some babies respond better to movement and vibrations or sound or visual cues. Keep in mind that this alternative technique might soothe your baby but not be as rewarding for you as a nice warm cuddle with your newborn.

MYTH: You have to stop breastfeeding to get your child to sleep through the night

Just as there is more than one way to crack an egg, the same is true for getting your child to sleep. In fact, breastfeeding your child at night can help her sleep as your night-time breast milk contains the sleep hormone melatonin. In those crucial first few months when baby is not producing her own melatonin breastfeeding can actually be a bonus! Use breastfeeding as a prop/cue and ensure you don't create a dependency. It's that's simple!

You can avoid creating a dependency on breastfeeding by split-feeding. This is a technique where you divide the feed into two, and introduce an activity in between. For example, you could feed your baby for 10–15 minutes before a bath and then for 10–15 minutes afterwards. This will ensure your baby does not fall asleep on the boob. Also, taking your baby off the boob just before she falls asleep is another little tip to avoid dependency. Just as your baby has fed for at least 10 minutes and begins to slow down on her sucking, you can ease your nipple from her mouth while she is still awake.

Chireal's Tip Bits

Pre-empt night feeds for both bottle- and breastfed babies and they *will* learn to sleep.

MYTH: Blackout blinds will mean your child will sleep

Yes, it's true that our body rhythm is regulated by exposure to light and dark, and yes, when we have an established sleeping pattern we tend to sleep better and for longer in darker rooms. However, babies and children have to be taught how to self-soothe and as night-time is the longest time our children are away from us, bedtime can be a time when our babies become anxious. If you have an anxious child or baby he will not sleep, no matter how dark it is. In fact, sometimes a room being too dark may be the cause of the anxiety. So it's important to remember that babies who are not able to ground themselves when they wake will cry and call out to be soothed. At times, a room being too dark can actually work against you. In fact, research has shown that red light and blue light help to provide good sleep.

> *Chireal's Tip Bits*
>
> Use blackout blinds for children who are not scared of the dark; use night lights to ease a child's anxiety.

MYTH: Putting your child to bed later will mean he will sleep later

I have always been confused by this myth. The body rhythm is like a clock set at particular times, so if your child is used to waking up at 5am putting her to bed at 9 or 10pm will mean that she will become sleep-deprived. The less sleep we have the fewer sleep hormones we produce, which means we are likely to sleep less. The answer is therefore that more sleep is better. Put your baby to bed earlier because sleep begets sleep. The more sleep your baby has, the more sleep your baby will want. Putting her to bed later may cause your child to become overtired, difficult to settle and make your situation a lot worse for a while, with potential tears and tantrums.

MYTH: Babies become addicted to dummies

Dummies, pacifiers, soothers ... no matter what you call them the mere mention of their name can strike fear in some people and positive elation in others. What we know to date is that some US research (Walsh et al, 2014) suggests that it is possible that using a dummy when putting a baby down to sleep may reduce the risk of sudden infant death syndrome (SIDS).

The theories as to why this is the case vary. Some say the active ingredient is the behaviour of the parents and their response to putting the dummy back in the baby's mouth after it has fallen out. The rationale here is that it is the parents' constant checking of their baby that prevents SIDS. The UK Department of Health, however, does not currently recommend dummy use as a way of reducing the risk of SIDS. We will always be surrounded by conflicting evidence, advice and new research so I would advise that you use the information at hand to make an informed choice, and be confident that you are making a decision to use or do something based on what is right for your family. Being confident in your needs and wants for your family and trusting your instinct is so important.

If you do decide to use a dummy with your child, you need to ensure it works well with your sleep routine. We know that babies like to suck and so for some babies and parents the dummy may be a suitable option to help soothe and limit distress. Here are my top tips on using a dummy as part of your bedtime routine and establishing a natural sleep pattern:

* Make the dummy part of your bedtime routine. Give it to your child at the right moment – after you have placed her to lie down in the cot/bed space.
* If you choose to use a dummy, wait until breastfeeding is well established (at up to about four weeks old). We know that overuse of a dummy reduces the number of breastfeeds a baby has. It also reduces the number of times a baby has a bottle but trust that you will learn what your baby needs – whether it's a bottle or a dummy.
* At around 6 to 12 months try to reduce the use of a dummy with a view to permanent removal.
* Teach your child to root and put the dummy back independently to avoid them depending on you to put it back in throughout the night. This can be done as soon as your baby has mastered hand–mouth coordination at around four months.
* If your baby doesn't want the dummy then leave it out.
* If your baby decides to spit the dummy out then leave it out.
* Avoid dummy neck cords as there may be a risk of strangulation.
* Only use one dummy at a time. Avoid the use of a rainbow of dummies over your baby's sleeping head.
* Keep the associations clear and use a dummy for bedtime sleeps only.
* Using an orthodontic dummy is best as it adapts to your baby's mouth shape. Add nothing (such as sweet liquid) and take nothing away (i.e. don't change the dummy in some way).

MYTH: Co-sleeping now will mean co-sleeping for ever

Some parents choose to co-sleep and some parents wish to but are worried that their children will co-sleep with them forever. I don't know of any self-respecting teenager who still sleeps with their parent. Mind you, I co-slept with my children and did get a visitor in my bed the day before A level results were due. The next night she went back to her room ... and now lives in her own flat while she studies at university. I don't think co-sleeping with your baby is a problem that will last a lifetime. So if that suits your family then by all means co-sleep in a safe way.

Co-sleeping has its benefits and there is an on-going debate as to whether parents should or should not co-sleep. My view is that this is a family choice and parents should feel confident to make the decision to co-sleep or not based on an informed choice. Research from The National Centre for Biotechnology Information suggests that bed-sharing, which leads to more breastfeeding, may be considered a protective factor against SIDS.* They reason that bed-sharing babies are breastfed more than babies who sleep separately from their parents. So in this instance sharing a bed may help reduce the risk of SIDS. However, we need to ensure our environment is safe and that we are acting in a safe manner when choosing to sleep with our babies. There are guidelines for safe co-sleeping for those parents who wish to share a bed with their child and these vary depending on which book or website you visit. I have listed the main themes for your ease.

(*http://www.ncbi.nlm.nih.gov/pubmed/9240802?dopt=Abstract)

Your baby should not share a bed with anyone who:

* Is a smoker
* Has consumed alcohol
* Has taken drugs (legal or illegal) that make them sleepy

Other things to note:

* Do not sleep on a sofa or in an armchair with your baby
* Avoid co-sleeping if your baby was born prematurely or was of low birth weight
* Keep your baby cool while he sleeps with you and avoid overheating. Remember if you co-sleep you will all be emitting body heat
* Keep your baby's face cover-free while sleeping and use loose natural fibre bedding

As our children get older and more able to move independently they will form all sorts of shapes and positions in bed and some may choose to turn on to their tummy. When they are this mobile this sleeping style is less of a risk. You may decide at this point to move him to his own room as you and your baby may sleep better apart.

Chireal's Tip Bits

Sharing a sleeping environment can promote a good healthy sleeping pattern for your child.

MYTH: Travelling or going abroad will break your child's sleep pattern

Those who know me well will confirm that I have a firm view that sleep can happen wherever you are, and that includes overseas. I believe in getting sleep while life happens, as opposed to putting life on hold while you try to get your baby to sleep, which can make your whole focus become on sleep and how the lack of it makes you feel so downbeat and broken. So I coach my clients to continue living and guide them through how they can get their babies sleeping no matter what time or what the environment is. The body rhythm is very adaptable so once you are confident and skilful you and your baby will learn to sleep while travelling, despite being between time zones! And I will show you how – see page 202.

> *Chireal's Tip Bits*
>
> Don't let 'sleep' issues stop you from getting out and living your life.

By busting some of the common myths we have shaken off some of the misnomers that surround sleep. The next stage in this process is understanding how your feelings, thoughts and behaviour impact on your baby's sleep, and learning how CBT can address this issue to be in a position to understand what the barriers are to your baby sleeping well. We need to address the underlying factor as to why your baby has yet to establish a natural sleeping pattern.

It is not enough to merely discuss concepts and practices that have been used in the past, we also have to prove the rationale and framework for the Gentle Sleep Solution. This will allow you to make an informed choice about whether this is the plan for you. I believe that it is but I need you on board. If you do not buy into it, then it's not going to work. The commonly held view is that many of our relational problems can be attributed to our thoughts, beliefs and values. It is my belief that by teaching you how to use CBT approaches, attachment tools and mindfulness you will be able to overcome your sleep problem. Allow me to provide the framework of how I will guide you and your family to solve your sleep problem using the framework of CBT, mindfulness and attachment tools.

Chapter 2

How to Read Your Child's Behaviour

Did you know: Breastfeeding helps babies develop more resilience in response to stress?

THEY SAY THAT BABIES DON'T COME WITH A MANUAL. I WOULD disagree: they don't come with a manual that we can easily read, but they come into this world with a manual that is written in a language we have yet to learn. They *are* the manual. I want to show you how you can learn your baby's language from birth onwards until such time we have taught them our own.

Our baby's development can be broken down into the areas of physical, social, cognitive and language development. In the first 12 weeks of your baby's life their reflexes, movement and sounds will guide you towards understanding their language.

By knowing how to read your baby's body language and interpret her cries you are able to meet her needs and limit her distress. A baby's main way of communicating verbally in the first years is through crying and while prolonged crying is not healthy for babies it would be unrealistic for us to expect that our babies won't ever cry; in fact, research shows that not all crying causes stress. Remember that your job is to calm your baby and limit their distress, but you can only do that if you know what their distress and need is. This is where you need to use the PAUSE method. You need to listen and hear the cry to decipher what your baby is actually saying to you.

The PAUSE method

Before you put your plan into action, I want to show you the PAUSE approach. PAUSE is an important lesson; it will stop you rushing in blindly to a situation without thinking. PAUSE will help you read your child's language, PAUSE will aid you in knowing what you will do and how you will do it, PAUSE is what every parent must do to become successful, PAUSE will allow you to calm yourself before you calm your child.

Prepare and plan your next move.
Have what you need with you and ensure you are in the right emotional state to calm your baby.

Assess
You want to be able to analyse the situation – what is actually happening – without being led by fear or worry. You need to do this so you know what you need to do and what your baby's needs are.

Understand what your child is trying to communicate to you.
Understand his cries and his body language.

Soothe
Be there to settle your baby in the appropriate way, teaching him to sleep independently.

Exit the room when your child no longer needs you or is asleep, whichever comes first.

My method works on the basis that you respond to your child's needs. If he calls, it's important that you PAUSE. Think about what he may be communicating, ask yourself the question: is what I am about to do helping or hindering sleep? If your baby is unwell, meet his need first, if he needs a nappy change meet his need, if he is hot/cold meet his need first. Then use the appropriate levels of responsiveness to calm him.

When you have asked yourself these questions and you have a clear idea in your head what is ailing your child, go in with the response that matches their level of distress (see page opposite). Start at the lowest level, which is your presence, and meet his need by working through the levels of responsiveness, stopping at the one that works and then returning back down the levels of responsiveness so that you eventually leave the room when your baby is calm. Engage his senses: use your presence which is the lowest but also a very powerful level, your proximity is the next stage up, then your touch, your breath, your voice and body and picking up is the highest and top-level intervention and reassurance response to calm your child. Once he is calm PAUSE: do you need to stay or can you leave?

Remember that you need to go in with the lowest level of response – your presence – at first and get your child used to being comforted that way and grade up or down based on his need. Remembering that before your child can accept your graded use of responsiveness you have to teach him to get used to this way of responding and communicating in the day time with general day-to-day interaction.

Whenever possible you should always attempt to calm your baby from within the cot. There may be times when you will have to pick your child up to calm him but limit this to no more than two times if he is older than three months. The 'pick up/put down' (PU/PD) method (see below) is a responsiveness type of calming that is in my view and experience designed for newborn babies until the age of 12 weeks. After this time your baby is able to tolerate less physical contact and be calmed away from your body. He is also at a very good stage of being able to learn his own idiosyncratic way of falling asleep and we should try to capture this window of opportunity. By picking him up too often we could be undoing the process of him self-soothing and learning how he likes to fall asleep. Babies who have passed this are still able to benefit from learning different levels if they have enjoyed PU/PD beyond this stage.

Whether you are a stay-at-home parent or a working one, you will spend a great deal of time with your baby. This time and your love connection makes you the best candidate to learn this new and unfamiliar language. I have every faith that this is a lesson that will be easy and quick for you to learn. All you need is your keen ears and eyes, and remember to PAUSE. By the second or third day of your baby's life you already know his cries/sounds from that of another baby. This proves that you have the capacity, ability and ear to learn your baby's cries. Some mothers will be able to know which cries mean pain, hunger or discomfort within the first two months, but for those who find it harder and for other caregivers, listen to the sounds and reflex sounds a newborn makes along with his body movement in the first three months of his life. This will speed up the learning process. These sounds and movements are mostly reflexes, which, as the baby gets past four months, almost completely disappear. By knowing what your baby is saying you are ready for success because you will know how to respond, enabling you to build a natural sleep pattern though nurturing.

We can also understand our new baby's behaviour by separating it into six states of consciousness:

1. active sleep
2. active crying
3. drowsy waking
4. fussing
5. quite sleepy
6. quite alert

These states are dependent on how healthy and happy your baby is and his physical responses, such as body movement, breathing and muscle tone, will vary depending on what state he is in. By watching your baby over a period of days, and noting down their varying states at different times of the day, you will begin to see a pattern building and you can use this to formulate your daily routine. You can therefore tailor your sleep plan based on your baby's needs and state of consciousness, as well as your family's composition.

Your baby's sleep cycle has not matured yet and so before he is four months he will sleep in cycles of between 30–50 minutes and require feeding every two hours or so. Breast milk is absorbed by the body faster than formula so some breastfed babies may require feeding more frequently than a bottle-fed baby. This knowledge will help you to feel more empowered and in control of shaping your baby's natural sleeping pattern.

Your baby's physical development

So what do we already know about our newborn's ability to move? We can learn the stages of our baby's ability to move based on their age using the top-down analogy. Our baby's physical development starts from the top and progresses all the way down to their feet – lifting their head and sucking come before sitting, and sitting and crawling come before walking.

0–3 months

At newborn to three months our baby's main movements are reflexes: he can lift and turn his head, clench and unclench his fists. In the early days, you can learn a lot from how your baby moves his head and the sound he makes when he does this.

4–6 months

When your baby reaches four months he will be able to move his head, hands and legs more meaningfully, and can track objects with his eyes. You can use this visual development to aid comfort, maintaining eye contact for example, or showing your baby pictures of you.

6–9 months

By six months your baby is able to roll, sit and hold things. This is another opportunity to begin to get your baby to use the dummy himself and self-root at night to put it back in. He is able to move around the cot and find his own way of getting comfortable. During this stage of development you should allow him as much freedom as possible, even though it may look like he is more wakeful. This is an important part of learning to self-soothe and settle.

9–12 months

Around nine months of age your baby is standing, attempting to walk and he can use his body in lots of ways to let you know how he is feeling and what he wants. He is able to stand in the cot and let you know he is not quite ready to go to sleep just yet. At this stage he also knows how to sit from a standing position, so we are again able to let him stand and sit freely at bedtime and roll with resistance.

12 months onwards

Around 12 months our babies may be ready to walk and this is an important phase in learning that he is separate from us as he can create distance through space by walking away from us and coming back. We can use this type of development to communicate that being away from us is okay and through setting boundaries build trust by coming back before he gets anxious.

Chireal's Tip Bits

You are the expert of your family: trust your instincts not your fear.

Reading your baby's physical cues

Your baby's cries and body language can offer clues as to what he needs and how he is feeling. As our babies get older and as our relationship with them grows stronger, and we feel more experienced and comfortable, we start to recognise his cries and needs more distinctly. But in the first few days and weeks of our babies' lives the sound that comes from their little bodies can be hard to make sense of. With your own acute ear and by understanding your baby's body language you will be able to recognise exactly what your baby really wants you to know and become your own sleep consultant. This in itself will hopefully fill you with all the confidence you need to embark on building a natural sleep pattern though nurturing your baby and changing the habits that have been unhelpful in the past.

Basic body language

	Hungry	Tired	Overstimulated	Bored
Head	Turns to side and cranes neck back	Moves from side to side		Turns away from object
		If in upright position, nods like a person asleep on a train		
Eyes		Red, bloodshot	Staring	
		Slowly close and spring open		
Mouth/ lips/ tongue	Lips pursed	Yawn		
	Curls tongue at the side			
Face				
Hands/ arms	Hands brought up to mouth trying to suck them		Flailing and very uncoordinated, may claw skin	Playing with fingers
Torso	Arches back, looking for breast or bottle			
Skin				
Legs		Strong, uncoordinated kicking		

Wind or pain	Cold	Self-soothing	Crying for too long	Over-heated	Wet nappy
The appearance of a scream but no sound, then a wail	Bottom lip quivers	Sucks tongue self			
Grimacing, scrunched up face, if lying down			Red veins at temple may stand out		
May also start to pant, roll eyes and make an expression that resembles a smile					
Flailing and very uncoordinated, may claw skin					
Arms shaking, slight tremor					
Squirms, moving bottom from side to side	Squirms, moving bottom side to side				Squirms, moving bottom side to side
Goes rigid	Shivers				
Blue fingers and toes	Blue fingers and toes		Clammy, sweaty	Clammy, sweaty	
	Tiny goose pimples		Blue fingers and toes		
Pulled up to chest					

Your baby's body language

Consult the body language table above to see what are the likeliest causes of your baby's movements.

Your baby's cries

Listen to the sound your baby makes just before feeding or calling out for a feed. The newborn's sucking reflex has been established and the tongue is pushed to the top of the mouth and as he opens his mouth sound comes out that will indicate that he is hungry. Watch out for when your baby yawns: sound is made in the reflex of a yawn which means, very simply, that your little bundle of joy is tired and ready for sleep. This one may be the quickest and easiest for us to know. During the day when your baby becomes bored or his body language shows discomfort, you will hear a sound as though your baby is frustrated before he launches into a full cry. When you hear this sound over a period of time, and you are sure that it is linked with the body movements in the chart above, then you can be sure that this sound is made when your baby is in discomfort. This can be anything from being bored, needing a nappy change, feeling cold or wanting a change of scenery.

When your baby is in pain you will hear a grunting sound which comes from the stomach; sometimes it may sound like wheezing. This sound is not hard to miss and will indicate that your baby is in pain. This could be due to acid reflux. Reflux, also known as gastro-oesophageal reflux or GOR, is the backwash of milk and irritating stomach acids against the sensitive lining of the oesophagus; mild reflux is recognised as spit up. Your newborn will draw his legs up or push them down and out, telling you that he is in discomfort. Because this sound may be at first hard to distinguish, you can look for body language signs that will almost certainly come with this pain/discomfort sound.

If I had a penny for every time we hear the phrase 'all babies are different' I would be on a permanent holiday. However, no matter how often we hear it, we still want our babies to be the same and act the same as other well-behaved babies that sleep all night (again another phrase I often hear that would make me very rich indeed). It's okay to be different and it's important to embrace that difference. Acknowledge that your difference makes you unique as long as that difference does not cause you or anyone any harm. Some babies cry, some cry more than others. Most babies up until three months will cry from 1–3 hours a day. Crying for any length of time can affect those that hear it and for lactating mothers it can trigger the let-down reflex and they start to leak milk. So our natural urge to save our sanity is to reduce the crying. If your baby cries for longer than three hours per day, he may have colic. Seek medical advice on how to manage this type of distress as colic can be a symptom of any one of a number of problems, most of which are easily solved. Research has shown that colic usually disappears after four months.

The evolution of your baby's language skills

Age	Range of cries	Alert to voice	Coos	Vowel sounds	Copies sounds	Babbles	Laughs	Responds to simple commands
0–2	☺	☺						
2–4	☺	☺	☺					
4–6	☺	☺	☺	☺				
6–9	☺	☺	☺	☺	☺	☺	☺	
9–12	☺	☺	☺	☺	☺	☺	☺	☺

As you can see from the table above the older your baby gets the less he relies on crying to communicate with you. Again he is learning just as you are so even more reason to PAUSE. This tells you that as time goes by you will have more and more clues as to what your baby may be telling you. Your baby is doing what is expected of him, and by trying to work out what he wants, so are you: remember you are doing the best job you can. As your child progresses through the stages of development, keep in mind that whatever stage or problem you are at, you will not be there for long and you do have the Gentle Sleep Solution tools to overcome it.

How to calm your baby

Just as you can be taught by your baby how to read his body language and his cries to meet his needs and promote the bond between you, so too can you use their sensory development to aid your ability to settle them and help them to establish a healthy sleeping habit. We do this through sight, sound, smell and touch. The golden key here is to know what sounds, smells and touch your baby likes and to use them when he is distressed. As your child grows, remember that his needs will change and so in order to keep him reassured and settling and sleeping well you should match the sensory aid/tool to his stage of development.

Sound

Sound is such a powerful tool. Your baby can hear even before he is born, and in the womb becomes used to the swishing sound of the inside workings of your body. Once he is born that swishing becomes a comforting sound, as is your voice and anything else you had him listen to when he was neatly tucked in your tummy. You can use these sounds to help soothe your baby, get familiar with his environment and mask external noise that may startle him. As your child gets older, he becomes more familiar with other types of sound, like the spoken word, traffic and normal household noise. Use this when you are trying to get your baby to sleep – use age-appropriate 'white' noise and soothing sounds based on your environment, and on your family's circumstances. A newborn baby will be soothed by sounds similar to those heard in the womb; a family living in the city will have different familiar sounds to a family living in a rural part of the country. An only child might be used to a quieter house, whereas a baby with older siblings may have become used to lots of noise. Sounds can offer reassurance to a child and we can use sound to help them enter into a new environment like a new home by playing familiar sounds in the background, or if you're travelling, habiting (getting your child familiar) to a sound can be very helpful as you are able to get them to settle and sleep no matter what the environment is. One thing is clear though – your baby prefers the human voice over all sounds, and your voice most of all.

Smell

Your baby's sense of smell is strong. Babies prefer what they know, and they know their parents, so it stands to reason that your baby loves how you smell. Babies' taste buds are acute from birth and they prefer the things that taste sweet. Breast milk is sweet so use the smell of breast milk to calm and soothe your baby: place a small amount of breast milk on a muslin or on your baby's bed sheets. If your baby is not breastfeed, transfer your own sweet smell by wearing a muslin or bed sheet for a while.

Touch

Affectionate touch and other nurturing behaviours appear to trigger the release neurotransmitters, like oxytocin and endogenous opioids (Kojima et al 2012; Weller and Feldman 2003). So we want to enhance and increase these hormones and chemical responses at night-time through touching our babies or allowing them to touch/suck for themselves, when we are helping our babies to sleep, whether with us or without us. Touch puts our babies in a good mood and also helps them to build up a tolerance and bounce-back factor from stressful situations. So the more you touch your baby the better he is able to deal with situations when you are not present. Other research hints that infant massage can reduce stress hormone levels (Underdown et al 2006). Remember that changes to the environment, such as loud shouting voices, feeling cold or being left alone in distress, can bring on a stress response in your child. By our responsiveness and by our actions, we can limit and reduce the number of stressful situations our babies are exposed to, for example, by masking external noises with calming noises, or limiting shouting (stopping shouting altogether is harder to achieve if you have lots of older boisterous children in the home). Keep your baby wrapped up and warm, especially at bathtime when you should keep them clothed until the very last minute. Also keep the space warm that you are putting them down to sleep in to minimise the difference and change in temperature. The idea is to create a seamless transition so the less changes to body temperature the better. By keeping your baby warm, snug and safe, you are limiting their distress.

Room temperature

Experts recommend that your baby's room should have a temperature of between 16–20°C. This can be hard to judge and get right. You can adjust your heating or your baby's clothing and bedding to ensure you have a temperature that is both safe and comfy for your baby. For example, you may choose to use light bedding or a lightweight well-fitting baby sleeping bag that is comfortable and safe for sleeping babies.

However, remember that, like adults, every baby is different and their requirements and temperatures will adapt and fluctuate depending on their well-being, mood or state, as well as the season. So while we remember the importance of knowing about overheating, checking your baby at regular intervals in line with when you feed (every 3–4 hours) will put you in control and you will quickly come to know if he is too hot and make the necessary steps to do something about it.

One of the ways you can check to see if your baby is too hot is by feeling your baby's tummy or the back of their neck. Having a room thermometer will help you keep an eye on the temperature of the room but not the temperature of your baby. Time your checks so that they are at the same time as feeds to alleviate any worries about waking your baby prematurely. Don't be misguided in thinking that the warmth or lack of warmth from their feet or hands is an accurate indicator. It is perfectly normal for the extremities on our little ones to be cooler. Your baby may well show signs of overheating by being sweaty and clammy. If this happens just remove a layer of clothing. Your baby is unable to regulate his body temperature so it is important that we do what we can to provide him with the optimal level of warmth so sleep can be waiting just around that corner. By the time your infant is two years of age he will begin to gain control over his body temperature .

A note of caution: going back to our 'all babies are different' mantra, taking all the research into touch into account and its benefit for babies, we know that not all babies like to be touched. Some babies' experience of touching is not always interpreted as pleasant or helpful, so it's important for us to know this, so that we don't take this to mean that our babies are rejecting our parenting, and also so that we can find other ways to soothe our baby and find out exactly what our babies like. We are fortunate because we have five senses to choose from and if touch is not for your little one then we can use the other four. Studies have shown that light caresses, which as adults we may like and enjoy, may not feel good to our young babies due to their brain still developing. Studies have shown that the older baby (10 months) can tolerate being tickled as pleasant, yet younger babies (2–6 months) cannot (Kida and Shinohara, 2013).

So a word to the wise: if your baby appears to shrink from light touch, try to touch more firmly. This is one of the reasons swaddling and patting the bottom to soothe newborns work so well. When you touch your baby always ensure you are accompanying it with a verbal reassurance, this will ensure that your baby is getting the maximum benefit from the touch.

Chireal's Tip Bits

When it comes to touching your baby be gentle, slow, and use moderate pressure.

Sight

Sight for your baby can be used as a powerful soothing tool. Your newborn prefers your face above all other faces and he prefers human faces to all other objects. Not only is your baby pre-programmed to love your face but to also be extremely sensitive to facial expressions. Communication is a two-way process and your baby is picking up signs on how he should feel from you, so smile and have an expression that is welcoming and positive as your baby will become distressed and emotional to a blank expressionless face and express a fear response to an angry, upset face. At six months your baby can pick up on angry and happy body language.

At birth your baby can see within a range of 8–12 inches, so in the first few weeks keep things close. At 4–6 months he is able to distinguish colour, so using blue night lights will help promote calm and red night lights will help promote sleep at this stage.

Your newborn's inner ear (vestibular) senses at birth allow your baby to respond to rocking and changes of position, and so rocking and movement are an effective way to soothe and parents should be encouraged to do this, as long as it's conscientious – to calm baby and not to put them to sleep.

Chireal's Tip Bits

Movement can be a more powerful soothing and calming technique over being held, so put baby down and attentively move/rock him in the cot.

Tips and tricks

- Thirty minutes before your bedtime routine, dim the lights and use essential oils to signal slowing down for bedtime
- Give clear signs and cues that your baby is going to bed soon, using visual aids, sound aids, touch and smell to set the scene
- Remind older children every 10 minutes that it is nearly time for bed
- Reduce stimulation, light, noise and activity
- Pack toys away out of sight and out of reach/cover them with a throw
- Make bedtime something to look forward to but in a calm fashion
- Get your child to view their bedroom as a safe and inviting place
- Use closed options ('You can have the green PJs or the blue ones')
- Don't ask your child questions like, 'Do you want to go to bed?' Instead use firm statements, such as 'It's time for bed, let's go.
- Once children are in bed use 'last chance saloon' to avoid excessive favours: last kiss, last hug, last wee wee
- Reward good behaviour at each stage of the bedtime routine
- Try not to say or do things you can't follow through on
- Have all the tools you need with you on a tray so you are prepared for night-time wakes and feeding

Chapter 3

Identify your child's underlying sleep problem

Did you know: Almost everything we know about sleep was learnt in the last 25 years?

HOW WE FEEL, WHAT WE FEEL, THE INTENSITY OF OUR FEELings and the changes to our emotions can profoundly shape and influence our babies' behaviour. This is essentially the model of CBT. Understanding this offers a golden key that will help you unlock the secrets of healthy sleeping. Being able to use your emotions in an effective way, managing your positive emotions and using them to calm your child and allow sleep to happen will put you in control and mean you are able to change the way your baby feels in any given moment. If you are able to do that then your child will learn how to self-soothe from you being a responsive, calm and authoritative parent. Once your baby is able to self-soothe she is in the prime position, state and mood to then fall asleep. Once your baby falls asleep in a calm, independent fashion her body clock will remember this, and over time (2–3 weeks) this becomes an established pattern. You will have successfully taught your baby to sleep well both night and day.

Knowing and being able to understand the connection between our thoughts, feelings, behaviours and body sensations is so important, as our children look to us for clues on how they should feel, react and behave in any given situation, and this is when cognitive behavioural techniques come into their own. For example, a baby may not know that she is happy until a parent smiles at her, or a child may not begin to cry unless she sees the concerned reaction on her caregiver's face. Newborn babies' heartbeats are regulated and mirror that of their parents' when they are held close (this is such an effective way of calming a baby). Our feelings, thoughts, behaviours and body sensations guide and teach our children how to behave, eat, play and, most importantly, sleep.

Now imagine you are nervous, angry, upset or frustrated – your heartbeat speeds up, you become tense and even hot. In this state you will not be effective in calming your baby; in fact, it will create the opposite effect, as your baby will mirror your feelings. A baby will and can pick up on these moods and the physiological sensations that are going through your body. This is not the optimal emotion needed for learning how to self-soothe and definitely not the right emotion for sleep.

The CBT model: vicious cycle of poor sleep

I want to help you discover that your emotions are managed by your thoughts and your behaviour. I also want to show you how you can gain control of your emotions just by being aware of your thoughts and changing what you do. In essence, this is the method of CBT.

When you're in the room and feeling emotional and stressed, sometimes your thoughts become negative and self-defeating, leading you to feeling like giving-up or trying new things. Negative thoughts can intrude, such as 'I'm doing something wrong', 'my baby will never sleep'. These thoughts increase your anxiety and your stress levels, and this is what I will call the vicious cycle of sleep.

We all have concerns and worries and these worries may drive us to behave in a way that is undesired, based on our feared prediction of what may happen. This means that rather than acting in a well-thought-out and therefore more effective way, our behaviour is led by fear. When we respond to our problems based on fear we behave in a way that is directly related to reducing the worry and the fear straight away, rather than focusing on finding a meaningful and effective long-term solution. We become trapped in this behavioural response and learn that this is the quickest and easiest way of helping us to feel better in the moment and become primed to respond in this way in the future should these similar feeling arise. In addition, this cycle that we are now heavily invested in supports our negative thoughts and confirms our feared predictions. Caught in such a cycle, we believe our actions are helping us. In reality what is happening is that our actions are maintaining the problem: we are keeping our problem going basing our reactions on our feelings, rather than on having a well-thought-out plan. Understanding how you get caught in this vicious cycle will give you great insight into how you can break the cycle and make meaningful significant changes to how you think, act and feel. Ultimately by having a plan for your baby's sleep and not being led by fear will help you to create a natural sleep pattern. This is why using CBT skills is so important.

Here I can explain the cognitive model for sleep in more detail. Your baby crying is a very good example of a trigger – this means every time your baby cries it makes you think something or feel something, and even do something. It would be very difficult for you to avoid your baby's cries. Some parents find hearing their baby crying so difficult it causes them distress. There is a very good evolutionary reason that our babies' crying makes us feel this way: so that we don't ignore them. However, if you get distressed every time you hear your baby cry, you are not in the best emotional state to calm her. The lesson here is not trying to avoid the trigger but manage your emotional response to the trigger. The idea is to be able to change your actions in response to the trigger. This means that we need to feel less distress or no distress when our babies cry. By doing this we are shaping our behaviour and that of our child, and importantly we are learning how to manage and regulate our emotions. In some situations we may be able to limit the intensity of the distress so that our child does not pick up on the strong negative emotions. In other situations we will be able to change our emotional state to a more positive one.

To illustrate this vicious cycle I have included a diagram below. At the top we have the trigger, which is connected to a negative thought. That thought is connected to an emotion, and

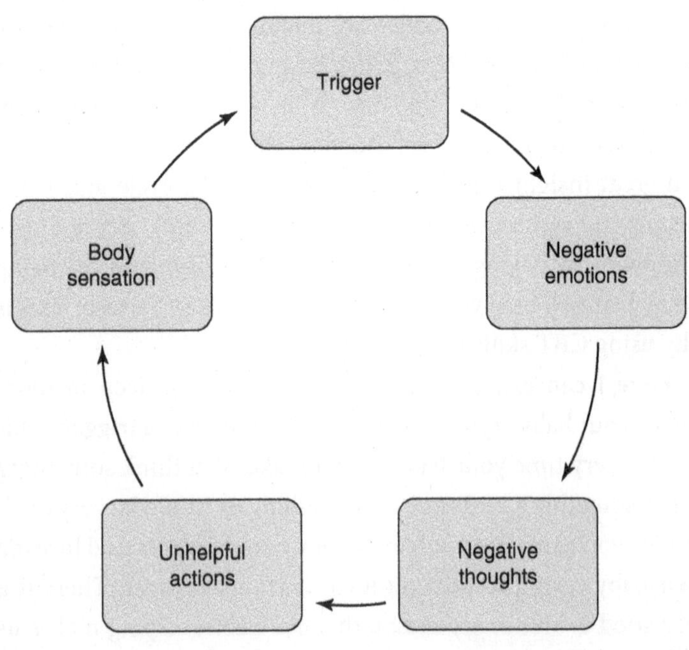

the emotion is connected to a body sensation. When we have intense feelings our bodies are primed to act in a way to reduce the discomfort and/or negative strong emotion. In this case by responding to reducing fear your reaction becomes an unhelpful behaviour. The vicious cycle continues as we form a pattern of behaving in the same way each time the trigger occurs. How we feel affects how we behave and how our bodies react. Over time we begin to develop a belief about the trigger – 'triggers are bad' – and this ensures that we are more sensitive to the trigger and more fearful of it and our natural reaction is to attempt to avoid that trigger. In reality our aim really should be on how we cope in difficult situations, which means we need to find out how we can best respond to triggers rather than avoid them completely.

Chireal's Tip Bits

You are your child's mirror: what you think and feel is what he will feel.

Now let's look at how this relates to sleep.

Many of you will be all too familiar with the vicious cycle of poor sleep illustrated above, but I want to show you not just how it works but also why it's hard to break the cycle.

Let me give an example: the trigger is a typical bedtime where you have been trying to get baby down for hours; the more you try the less it looks like your baby is going to sleep. The thoughts that run through your mind are plentiful, but the main ones are that this is pointless and that your baby will never sleep. The more you think this the more you notice that you are intolerant, frustrated, distressed, tired and even sad. As you notice these feelings your body reflects how you feel and you become tense, your heart may be beating rapidly and the more you notice it the more your thoughts keep telling you that what you are doing is not working and you should give up. As this vicious cycle continues the intensity of the thoughts and feelings build, and the more this happens the more your child is aware of how you are feeling – she is picking up on your body sensations and is less likely to sleep as a result. Your behaviour during this time reflects your feelings, you give up, you may even be crying, you may try rocking, feeding, turning on the lights or taking your child out of the room. You may even have resorted to driving them around in the car. This behaviour moves your child so far from sleep that the process keeps going and becomes, over time, a learned response for you both.

It would make logical and reasonable sense that over time, because you are struggling with your child's sleep and everything you are doing doesn't seem to work, you begin to pay more attention to the negative thoughts that are in your head, for instance, 'I am not a good enough mum' or 'This is all my fault'. If you begin to believe this, then I can easily understand why you might fear triggers, why you would want to avoid the trigger and why that trigger of your baby not sleeping would cause you to feel upset and lose hope. It makes sense because so far this has been your experience, it makes sense because nothing has changed and it makes sense because the vicious cycle of poor sleep just keeps on going.

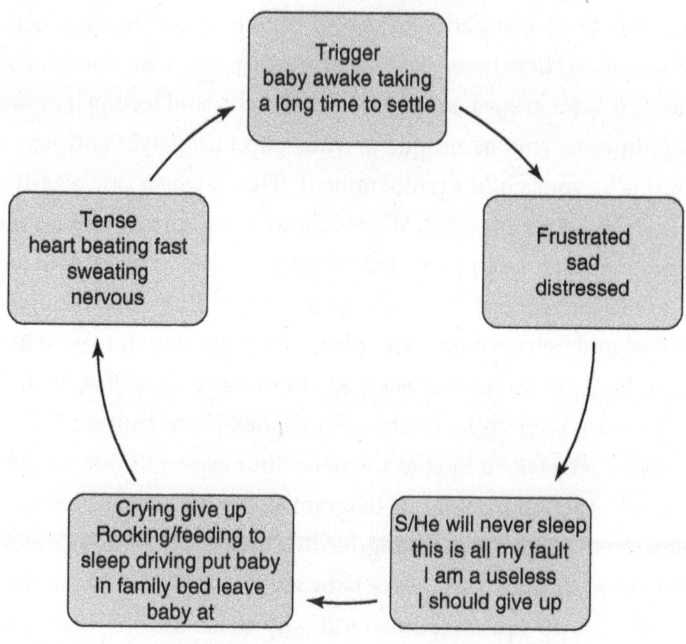

What keeps my child's sleep problem going?

If we know what is keeping the cycle going, we can stop it and change it. If we can stop it and change it then that forms part of our plan of action – it's our pathway that leads to change. The other golden key is your behaviour: what you are doing when you are triggered by your child's behaviour, and what you are thinking and feeling when you are trying to actively respond to your child. Write down what happens when you meet that trigger and what you do. Get familiar with your emotions and thoughts during the moments of putting your child to sleep. Ask yourself: how does this make me feel, what am I thinking in this very moment. Be honest, be detailed and be mindful. Being mindful is taking a moment to breathe, to look at your situation with a clear eye, to be rational and not overwhelmed with emotion, to be attentive to your situation in the here and now. There are no right or wrong answers here – this is personal to you. Your friends may have the same trigger as you but the thoughts and feeling it evokes is unique to you; as unique as your parenting style and just as unique as your child's temperament. This is why a one-size-fits-all method does not work. We are about to build your own unique family-specific sleep plan. This sleep plan will be successful and you will be successful because you are detailing your thoughts, feeling and behaviours, you are becoming more in tune with how your body sensations affect your mood and how that in turn impacts on your child, be she spirited, flexible or cautious.

Now let's take a look at the behaviour aspect of our model – this is the action part. In the diagram above the parent's response was: Crying, Give up, Rocking/feeding to sleep, Dummy, Driving, Put baby in family bed, Leave baby alone. I will take two of these behaviours to illustrate how and why these actions keep your sleep problem going. Let's first take a look at rocking to sleep:

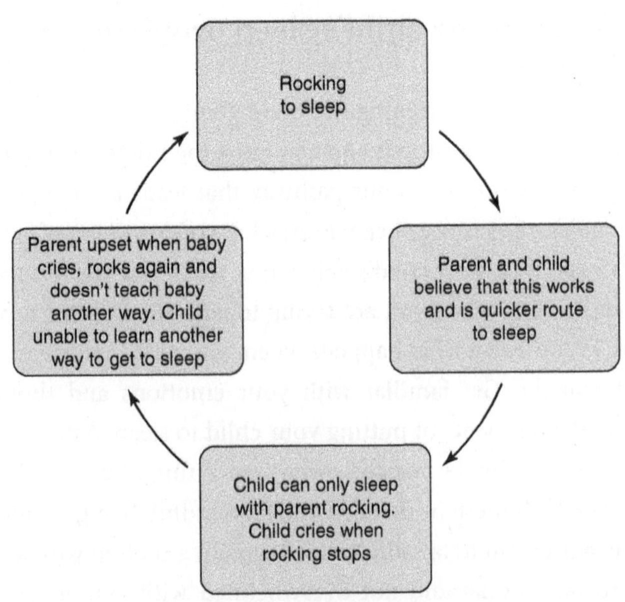

As you rock your baby to sleep, you and your child learn that this works, it's quick and your baby likes it so there are no tears. So the reasonable thing to do here is to continue rocking your child to sleep. Over time your baby learns, through association and conditioning, that rocking to sleep is the only way he can get to sleep. This action usually involves a parent and the child learns that the best thing to do when parents stop rocking is alert them to this event by crying. This triggers the parents into action and they continue rocking. The baby has learnt that his parents are triggered into action (rocking by the child's cry). Meanwhile, the parents become upset if the child cries and as they have a natural urge to stop the crying and discomfort they carry on rocking. During this critical phase neither child nor parents have the space or opportunity to learn, teach or think about trying something else. The opportunity to teach the baby another way to fall asleep is lost and so the pattern of unhelpful behaviour continues. The action part of the cycle – our behaviour – becomes the maintenance cycle of your vicious cycle. This is the part that keeps your problem going.

Here's another example of a vicious cycle using the dummy as the main behavioural response to the trigger of baby not going to sleep:

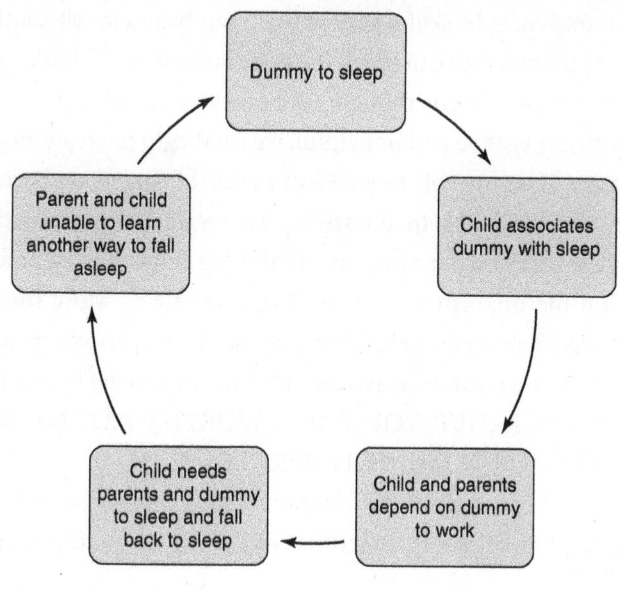

The CBT sleep cycle of change

I have worked with many families over the years and I know that sharing with them the vicious cycle of their current situation can be difficult. It's hard to look at the trap that you are in and the very cyclical nature of it can make you feel like there is no way out. There is a way out, however, and I wouldn't be doing the work I am doing if there were no solution to your and every other parent's sleep problem. Before we discover how we begin to break the cycle, I want to inject a little bit of hope and show you what our cycle of change looks like.

We can break the cycle in two ways. The one we have been discussing in detail is behavioural. We can break the cycle of poor sleep by behaving differently: by responding in a different way we open up a window of opportunity to show our babies a new way of sleeping, we begin to exercise our other muscles that will help our babies sleep. We open up the opportunity for new learning, for us and our babies. We begin to learn that we can use other techniques to soothe our babies that are more suitable and sustainable. We teach ourselves to be skilful and we teach our babies to self-soothe.

The other way we can break the cycle is the way we think – our thought process. If our thoughts are more balanced and helpful, rather than negative and unhelpful, we can begin to create a cycle of change. If we are able to establish a cycle of change we become more compassionate to ourselves, we create a compassionate cycle that becomes our new way of thinking and behaving and we open up the opportunity for our babies to sleep. More importantly, we create a new belief that is more accurate to who you are and where you want to be as a parent. That new belief is this: IT'S NOT YOUR FAULT, YOU ARE A WORTHY PARENT AND YOU ARE DOING THE VERY BEST YOU CAN.

As you can see from the diagram below, the trigger remains the same. The trigger is something you will learn to tolerate and understand in a different way. You will no longer live in fear of the trigger but will instead arm yourself with the tools and thinking patterns that will determine your success.

We are now going to begin the task of breaking the vicious cycle. We are going to look at triggers and decide that we shall respond to them in a considered and balanced way. Through this process you will become more aware of what your individual triggers are for you and your family.

As we build a more compassionate cycle of change you will see that the thoughts are balanced and helpful, rather than negative. As a result the emotions are less intense and may be more positive and the behaviours are more desirable ones that are helpful. So let's look at what that same cycle of change looks like when we match it to our sleep problem:

Compassionate cycle of successful sleep training

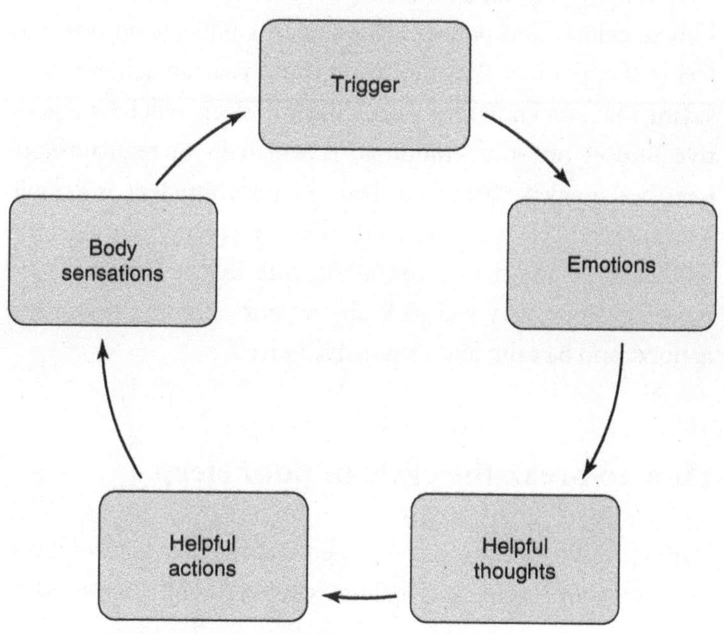

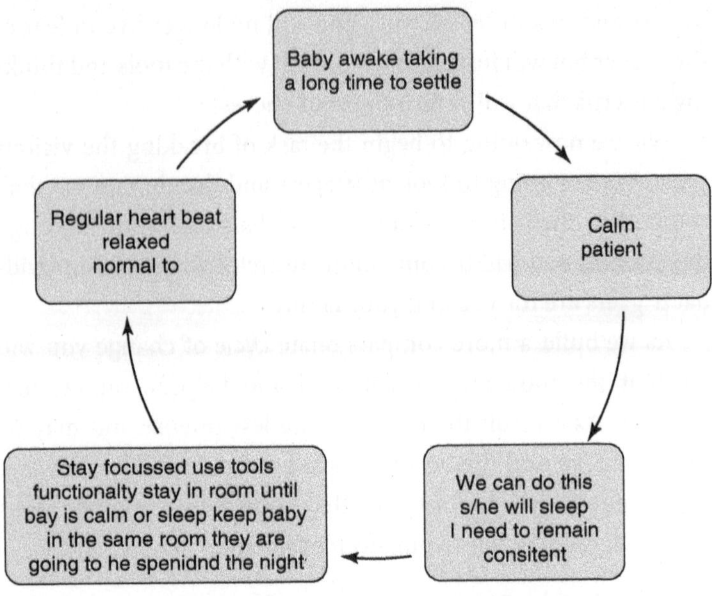

Thinking you can do this helps to make you feel more determined, calmer and patient. This in turns impacts on how you feel in the moment. The more you think you can achieve sleep, saying that you know that your child will sleep, will have a positive impact on your emotions. It will help to regulate your heartbeat and your behaviour will be more consistent as a result. You are less likely to flit between different types of solutions; you will act in a way that is confident, sure that your actions are working. Your baby will pick up on your calm and responsive actions, and be calm and responsive herself.

How to break the cycle of poor sleep

In the previous section we have seen that in order to change our behaviour and shape our babies' sleeping habits, we need to change the way we think and respond to our babies. You now know that you can manage the way you feel and create a state that is conducive to helping your child sleep. You are fully prepared and confident to now make those changes.

It is possible to break the cycle of poor sleep by putting into action a new way of thinking and behaving. Just by changing the way you look at sleep and how you approach your child's sleep is enough to break that painful cycle of doing what appears to work in the moment but actually keeps your problem going.

I do realise that for some parents it may be very hard to change the way they respond to their child, as it can be hard to accept that doing anything different, or even thinking differently, can make that much of a difference and the mere thought of changing your routine can feel very risky indeed.

Don't worry: we are still at the very early stages of your understanding, and in order for you to not be too overwhelmed, I am going to suggest that you begin to write things down. This is helpful for many reasons: it helps the learning process, and you will build your understanding of your problem at the same time you are building your plan. You will be amazed at what you discover about yourself and your family as you fill in each box. The form below is what we call a formulation, which is a fancy word for 'understanding your problem'. I have devised a formulation that relates to sleep.

I have included a blank CBT formulation in the appendices to fill in which will be the essential structure of your plan, along with a worked example. You will soon be able to see in black and white what your specific problem is and the areas that need to change.

CBT sleep formulation

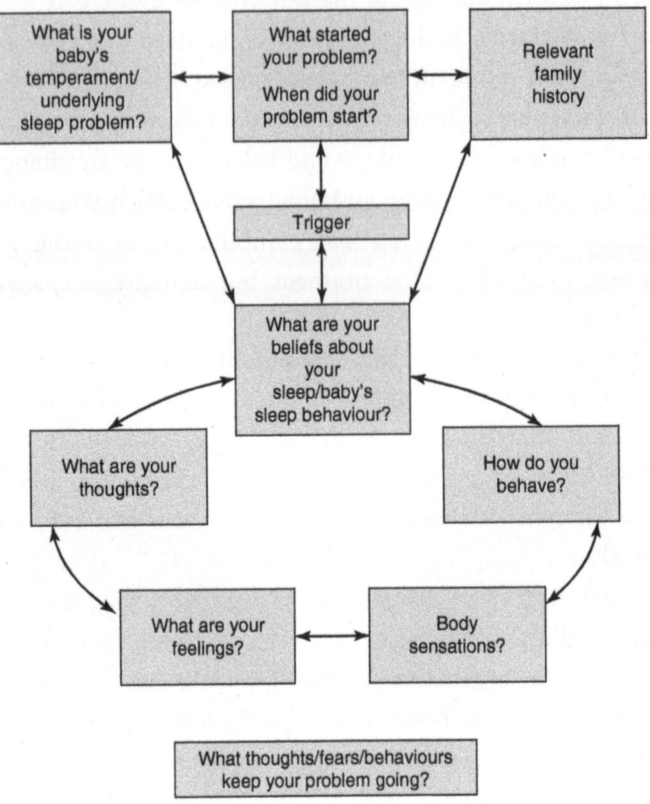

Action points

The way I look at it is this: change your view, change your behaviour and you will change your child's sleeping pattern. You have no guarantee that this will work, and far be it from me to try and convince you. All I ask is that you consider this. You have been on a path with your old behaviour, let's call it Plan A. You already know the consequences of what you get by using Plan A, your old way of thinking. By staying on this path you are fully aware that it doesn't get you to where you wish to be. So I am just going to ask you to consider Plan B – the new way of thinking and behaving. I ask that you be curious, that you take a small step towards the unknown with an air of curiosity and questioning. If all else fails there is nothing wrong with you going back to your old way of thinking and behaving. So take this journey with me and let's see if by putting the gentle sleep system into practice we can begin to change your child's sleeping habit for the better.

Chireal's Tip Bits

By knowing our weaknesses we can make them our strengths.

You are only part way to having all the tools you need to help your baby's sleep. I have explained the CBT model and how this relates to your feelings and emotions. We now need to look at the real reason your baby isn't sleeping before we can build that very important plan. Is it anxiety, dependency, sleep-cycle body rhythm issues, or a mixture of all three?

Anxiety

If your child's underlying sleep problem is anxiety your goal will be to help your child feel reassured in the day and in the night, when you are there and when you are not there. You will achieve this by first thinking about changing your child's environment, taking things out or putting things in that may help your child feel safe and comfortable and grounding them in the senses of sight, sound, smell and touch. You will also need your baby to know that their room is their space by spending time in the room away from sleep time and so getting them to take ownership of their room and build a positive association with it. The more time spent in the room together sharing lovely bonding time will help your child realise that this is a safe space and one that is okay to be in.

You will also need to get your child feeling okay in their room when you are in it or out. This can be achieved by leaving your presence in the room when you are physically not there: leaving a muslin with your smell or breast milk on it, having photos in the room, recording your voice and playing it back to her or give her a transitional object such as a comforter or another item that she likes. You will then need to change how you respond to your baby, using different levels of reassurance based on your baby's level of distress: the top-level reassurance would be to hold and pick up your baby and the lowest level would be your presence and the PAUSE method (see pages 36–38). Once you have done this you can begin your bedtime routine and implement the next changes. The main thing to note is that there should be an overlap of your presence and the new items you have given your child. It is important that you stay with your child to ensure that they have accepted the new transitional objects and they have a positive association with their environment. Your presence during this time is key and will usually take three to four days to secure. Based on your child's level of anxiety and the ease to which they accept change, and their temperament, the time may be longer or shorter. Once your baby has accepted the new changes you can then begin your gradual retreat over a period of one to two weeks.

Dependency

The goal with a child who is dependent on you is to get her to accept a set of routines and conditions that do not involve you or your presence in order to be maintained. The main part of your plan will be to help your baby self-soothe: instead of giving your baby the comforter she needs to sleep, help her self-root for it; instead of popping the dummy back into your child's mouth, place it next to her hand and guide it to her mouth. Trigger the learning for her to become dextrous enough to do the whole motion by herself. If your child is dependent on the breast or bottle your plan will be about taking your baby off the breast or bottle before she sleeps and pre-empting all feeds (see page 173). If your baby is dependent on being rocked to sleep you will use the PAUSE method and functional levels of responsiveness to get her used to soothing with your guidance but falling asleep independently (see pages 36–38). Your aim with a child who is dependent is to always give her something to replace the thing you are taking away. This method is about shaping behaviour through learning and reward through bonding and love.

Sleep cycle

When your baby's underlying sleep problem is to do with her circadian rhythm you will need to introduce and employ behaviours that are about having a routine, following the sequence of event rule to reset her body clock, and then using the PAUSE method and varying levels of responsiveness which match the levels of distress your child is displaying to help embed the changes and maintain them.

So what is stopping your child from sleeping? My quiz will help you find that answer.

Sleep quiz: the Chireal sleep measure

This short quiz will help you identify the underlying reason your child is not sleeping. We can then use your answers to build a plan that is unique to your child's temperament and the roles you are playing in your family to help your child gain a healthy sleeping habit.

Note: This quiz is designed to provide you with a quick and easy assessment of your child's sleeping issue. By completing the questions below you will discover what your child's main underlying sleep problem is. This will allow you to effectively target the real reasons your child is not sleeping, meaning greater success.

Dependency	Not at all	Only occasionally	Sometimes	Most of the time
My baby will only go to sleep sucking/rocking/being held	0	1	2	3
My baby wakes frequently and at different times throughout the night and day	0	1	2	3
My baby has always had problems falling asleep and/or staying asleep	0	1	2	3
My baby needs specific objects present in order to sleep	0	1	2	3

	No Issue/Mild	Mild/Moderate	Moderate/Severe
Answers	0–4	5–8	9–12

Anxiety	Not at all	Only occasionally	Sometimes	Most of the time
My baby is distressed whenever I leave the room	0	1	2	3
My baby needs to hold my hand/hair in order to fall sleep	0	1	2	3
My baby is clingy during the day and night	0	1	2	3
My baby prefers one parent to settle to sleep and give comfort	0	1	2	3

	No Issue/Mild	Mild/Moderate	Moderate/Severe
Answers	0–4	5–8	9–12

Sleep Cycle	Not at all	Only occasionally	Sometimes	Most of the time
My baby wakes at roughly the same times each night	0	1	2	3
My baby is an early riser	0	1	2	3
My baby takes a long time to settle at night	0	1	2	3
My baby has had periods of time when she has slept well	0	1	2	3

	No Issue/Mild	Mild/Moderate	Moderate/Severe
Answers	0–4	5–8	9–12

Your results	Score	Severity
Dependency		
Anxiety		
Sleep Cycle		

The item that has the highest score will be your main focus for change. In most cases where you tackle anxiety or dependency first, over time the sleep cycle will adjust organically as a consequence and you do not need to target this separately. When sleep cycle issue is the main and only problem then this should be your first action point.

Now you have identified why your baby won't sleep, I will coach you using mindfulness and attachment tools to move you forward as these are the essential tips on how to change your baby's sleeping pattern in a nurturing way.

Dependency relates to associations your baby has developed over time and therefore in order to break your cycle you will need to focus on helping your child learn new associations that are sustainable when you are settling at bedtime and throughout the night. So if, for example, your child is dependent on rocking, you would use rocking only when your baby is upset: this will allow her to get used to being calmed by the rocking and focus on going off to sleep once she is calm. This works the same for a dependency on feeding to sleep: your plan would be to work on your thoughts around the sleep issue, then help your child learn to sleep by withdrawing the feeding using, for example, split-feeding (see page 26).

With anxiety-related barriers to sleep, your aim is to help your baby feel reassured; you are using the attachment techniques of closeness and responsiveness to reassure your baby and once she is calm allowing her to fall asleep. You may also employ the use of leaving a piece of you behind and grounding her in your sight, sound and smell to help your baby feel safe and secure.

With sleep cycle barriers to sleep you will need to use a consistent approach by applying reassurance techniques in a functional and graded way.

This plan is specifically designed to work most effectively for babies aged 0–2 years. For the key areas of the sleep process I have described ways that you may handle them based on the result you have from the quiz.

Bedtime settling

For successful bedtime settling use what you know about your child's sleep issue. For sleep-cycle issues it means employing consistent bedtime cues, for the anxious baby it is about reassurance and tailoring the environment, for babies who are dependent it's about applying the right behaviour in a responsive way. Ensure your bedtime settling includes comfort in the right places, match the level of parenting to the level of distress and use a sequence of events to let your baby know what is happening and what is about to happen. Using all these strategies and settling at bedtime in the place your baby intends to spend the whole night is the recipe and plan for success.

Wakes at night

When attending to your child at night use the PAUSE method and the levels of responsiveness. Over the weeks you can begin to reduce the level of contact and plan your exit strategy. Once your baby is able to settle with either just your presence or verbal reassurance, she has learnt to self-settle.

Feeds at night

Use pre-emptive feeding for all night feeds. Drop night feeding when your child shows that she no longer requires these feeds. This may be determined by her age, how well she feeds during the day and/or rejection of the night feed. Parents who are unsure whether their child is ready to drop feeds can test this out by dropping the night feed over three nights. If the child sleeps well and/or settles well then you can be sure she no longer needs the feed. If she becomes harder to settle and/or becomes distressed this is an indicator that the night feed is still required.

Night feeding

Babies need feeding during the night for the sake of nutrition, comfort and the closeness they get by being with you. This very primal and necessary need is not the enemy of sleep and remembering this at night-time can really help you feel more accepting of your baby's wakes rather than viewing the wakes as your enemy. Embrace and accept that your baby is doing exactly what she is meant to and so are you. Enjoy, respond and nurture her into a calm and relaxed state and I guarantee you sleep will happen as a natural and beautiful consequence.

Your newborn baby will sleep through most noise and activity, though a sudden noise might wake her. A baby who seems very sleepy a lot of the time and who doesn't wake to feed may be ill, so don't assume a baby like this is 'being good'. Contact a health professional or the Naturally Nurturing Sleep clinic if you're worried (see resources).

Feeds during the day

To ensure that you are balancing feeds well, allow your baby to feed well during the day and that you have more daytime feeds than night-time feeds.

Chapter 4

Get your mind on your side

Did you know: Encouraging young children to sleep alone is a fairly recent practice within Western society?

THE FIRST AND MOST IMPORTANT STEP IN BEING ABLE TO MAKE a change and resolve a problem is acknowledging that one exists. If your child is not sleeping then it means you are not sleeping. It can take people many years of suffering from poor sleep before they feel ready to seek help to establish a better sleeping habit for their family. In recent years there has been an encouraging growth in parents seeking sleep help with their baby at an earlier age.

By getting your mind on your side I am talking about challenging your negative thoughts around your baby's distress or sleep disturbance. In this chapter, I will show you how to use CBT skills to change your thinking so that it is more balanced and will support your efforts of behavioural change. By getting your mind on your side you are essentially working on destroying your barriers to successful natural sleep patterns for yourself and your family. You will change your unhelpful negative thoughts to more helpful and positive thoughts.

Many people feel isolated and alone with their sleep problems, and most have a belief that their sleeping habit or problem is all part of the role of parenting and accept that they will never get sleep and endure the consequences of that mindset. Others will have tried many methods to help them to sleep before they talk to a professional. Many parents become confused by all the resources out there and some go for years before they speak to a sleep expert due to shame and embarrassment about not knowing how to help their child sleep.

The issue is this: you want your child to sleep because she needs to, and you want to sleep for the very same reason, so the sleep problem is not just about how your baby sleeps but how you perceive how well you sleep too!

The very first question my clients ask me is: 'What is good sleep?' The answer is slightly more complex than at first glance. 'Good sleep' is very much an individual perception. When we wake up refreshed and ready for the day then it is generally believed that we have slept well. On the other hand, if we wake up tired and groggy we tend to feel that we have not had a good night's sleep, and if we experience pain on waking up we tend to feel that our night was a bad one. Commonly, most of us think that if we get less than 6–8 hours then we have not had a good night's sleep and we tend to calculate how much sleep we will be able to get based on the time we need to get up in the morning. Before we even go to bed we may be telling ourselves, 'I won't get a good night's sleep tonight.' Ultimately, the question of a good night's sleep is based on so many different variables that are affected by how we think, how we feel, what we believe and how we behave.

While this may be a good theoretical discussion, it doesn't help understanding 'why' or provide any insight as to how I as a clinician would calculate and understand what good sleep is. Universally, we tend to talk about our experience of sleep and use a formulation of quality of sleep – which includes quantity – as a benchmark to answer this question. It's important to mention that our perceptions on our sleep and the beliefs that surround it are crucial to acquiring and maintaining healthy sleeping habits. Sleep evades almost one in two people, that's 45 per cent of the population who suffer from some form of sleep-related issue, so you are certainly not alone. We need to redress the balance as I reject the notion that insomnia and poor sleep are a rite of passage for parents. I firmly and vehemently believe that you can have a baby and have good sleep too.

Let me ask you a question: do you think it's your job to put your baby to sleep? A silly question you may think, but bear with me for a second. If you answered yes, I now want to ask you another question: how does it make you feel when your child does not go to sleep or doesn't sleep well? I would imagine not very good, am I right? Now, what if I were to say it was not your job to put your child to sleep, rather to provide the right environment and to guide your child to sleep. If you believed this and your child had poor sleep, how do you think you would feel? Not as bad as before, I'm guessing. My point is simple: by changing your view on your role, you create a whole new experience. This view moves you to feel more empowered to help your child rather than feeling as though you have failed.

I know how hard you are working and the bloody good job you are doing, but sleep has become this big monster for you that gets in the way of you noticing any of your strengths and successes. So let me remind you of how well you are doing. To get this far with very little sleep tells me that you are a strong character and that you are determined and dedicated to support your family's well-being.

Chireal's Tip Bits

Change your outlook and you change your outcome.

In the CBT sleep formulation, the connection between situation, feelings, thoughts, body reaction and behaviour are examined. The diagram on page 66 teaches that how you understand your problem has a beneficial and direct link on the effect on how you cope. The different aspect of your situation (your baby's poor sleep) and how you feel (exhausted) and how this makes you react (rocking) and the impact it has on your body (heart racing, tense) all play an essential part in what we refer to as your formulation, the conceptualisation of your own specific and unique situation. What is so wonderful about the CBT approach to understanding your problems is that your solution, your plan, falls right from the formulation, which is our vicious sleep cycle and our cycle of change. What do I mean by this? Well, you can see that by working on each area of the cycle you are able to change it to suit your need; you know that if you have an unhelpful thought or an unhelpful behaviour you will need to change these to more helpful ones. All you have to do then is use the attachment tools and your thoughts record of helpful thoughts and you have started to devise your own plan.

Overcoming fears

As if you didn't have enough to worry about being a parent and trying to get your baby to sleep, what happens when he finally drifts off? Once you have successfully got your little darling to sleep there is no time for you to enjoy that success and relax before another worry pops into your head: will he be okay *while* he sleeps?

Thankfully Sudden Infant Death Syndrome (SIDS) is still pretty rare. In the UK around 270 babies die from SIDS each year and, while it is a huge concern and one death is one too many, the risk of your baby dying from SIDS is low. We can manage some of our anxieties so they are highly reduced by taking some very simple steps. We still don't know the exact cause of SIDS, but what we do know is that the highest risk is between 0–6 months and the risk goes down to zero by year one.

Safe sleeping falls into three basic tips:

* Back to sleep: Placing your baby on his back when he is sleeping in his cot
* Room-sharing: Sleeping in the same room as your baby until he is at least six months old
* Bed-sharing: Having a cot that is attached to the family bed will help your baby to mirror your natural sleep pattern

Chireal's Tip Bits

Research states that breastfeeding mothers get more sleep.

Let's talk a little about what you can do to keep your baby safe and keep you reassured.

We have learnt how to manage our emotions so that we are tapping in to the healthiest and most helpful emotions that our babies will pick up on and use to help manoeuvre to a place of safe and delicious sleep. This is one of the most important keys to unlocking your success.

Fears are disabling. When fear is your predominant emotion, you are led by fear, motived by fear and maintained by fear. Fear takes you down a path you know you really don't want to go, like driving your baby in the car for hours because you are fearful your baby will cry or may disturb your other children or, worse still, your neighbour. You fear you are not doing enough to help your little one sleep so you read everything, talk to everyone and feel even more de-skilled as a parent. We are so fearful we may make things worse – we keep rocking our babies to sleep even though we know that this is problematic in our sleep routine.

The examples above show you how fear leads, becomes the motive for, and maintains our problems. We are moving towards change and we are going to be successful in making those sleep changes and gaining a healthy sleeping habit. In order to achieve this we need to overcome our fears – all our fears on, around and about sleep – letting go of the beliefs that keep you trapped. Trust that you are the best person for this job – you know yourself and your child and most importantly you know what you want.

This plan does not require you to give up the things you want to do with your baby. It requires you to let go of one thing: your fears. Get a piece of paper and start to write down what it is you want. If you want to co-sleep, then that's what you should do. If you want to continue to breastfeed then that's what you should do. If you want to end breastfeeding and sleep separately from the baby, then that's what you should do. We will get your baby to sleep around your wants. My message is simple: know what you want, write it down, focus on your needs and that of your family and make sleep happen. This is not a give-up method but rather a skill-up method. You will become a master of your family's sleep needs by discovering how you can effectively communicate with your baby to calm, soothe and help him learn how to fall asleep.

I would urge you to listen to your inner voice, and do what you feel is reasonable and safe, remembering that how you parent your child is up to you and you know what you can live with. Don't forget what is important to you and what it is you want from a situation. Try not to feel pressured by the wealth of information around safe sleeping and the critical rules of the should-and-should-not brigade. Be safe but also be kind to yourself.

Tips for safe sleep

- Place your baby on her back to sleep
- Keep your baby smoke-free during pregnancy and after birth
- Place your baby to sleep in a separate cot or Moses basket in the same room as you for the first six months
- Breastfeed your baby, if you can
- Use a firm, flat, breathable natural fibre mattress in good condition

Did you know: Sleeping on the job is acceptable in Japan? It is viewed as exhaustion from working hard. Some people fake it to look committed to their job.

How to overcome unhelpful thoughts

Thoughts are the cognitive element to the CBT model

In the previous chapter I described the vicious sleep cycle and how your thinking can keep you trapped and how your behaviour can keep your problem going. I also explained that by changing your thinking you could break the vicious cycle and create a more compassionate one. I want us to explore this further here because often before we start to change our baby's pattern of sleep, our way of thinking sets up roadblocks. Also, while we are implementing our sleep plan, our old pattern of thinking can come back to try to throw us off track. I want to teach you how you can keep on the path to good healthy sleeping by first identifying what your unhelpful thinking style is.

Identify your unhelpful thinking style

When a person experiences an unhelpful emotion (e.g. depression or anxiety), it is usually preceded by a number of self-statements and thoughts. Often there is a pattern to such thoughts and we call these 'unhelpful thinking styles'. We use unhelpful thinking styles as an automatic habit, something that happens out of our awareness. When a person consistently and constantly uses some of these styles of thinking, they can often cause themselves a great deal of emotional distress. A number of 'unhelpful thinking styles' are described below. As you read through them, you might notice some thinking patterns and styles that you use consistently. Some of these styles might sound similar to one another. They are not meant to be distinct categories but to help you see if there is a kind of pattern to your thoughts.

Mental filter

This thinking style involves a 'filtering in' and 'filtering out' process, a sort of 'tunnel vision', focusing on only one part of a situation and ignoring the rest. Usually this means looking at the negative parts of a situation and forgetting the positive parts, and the whole picture is coloured by what may be a single negative detail.

Jumping to conclusions

We jump to conclusions when we assume that we know what someone else is thinking (mind-reading) and when we make predictions about what is going to happen in the future (predictive thinking).

Personalisation

This involves blaming yourself for everything that goes wrong or could go wrong, even when you may only be partly responsible or not responsible at all. In extreme cases, you might take 100 per cent responsibility for the occurrence of external events.

Catastrophising

Catastrophising occurs when we blow things out of proportion, and we view the situation as terrible, awful, dreadful and horrible, even though the reality is that the problem itself is quite small.

Black-and-white thinking

This thinking style involves seeing only one extreme or the other. You are either wrong or right, good or bad, and so on. There are no in-betweens or shades of grey.

'Shoulding' and 'musting'

Sometimes by saying 'I should…' or 'I must…' you can put unreasonable demands or pressure on yourself and others. Although these statements are not always unhelpful (e.g. 'I should not get drunk and drive home'), they can sometimes create unrealistic expectations. For example: my baby *should* sleep from 7 to 7. While some babies may do this, this would be an unrealistic expectation of a newborn that would cause you huge levels of frustration and distress if you were not able to 'make' your baby sleep in this pattern.

Overgeneralisation

When we overgeneralise, we take one instance in the past or present and impose it on all current or future situations. If we say 'You always…' or 'Everyone…' or 'I never…' then we are probably overgeneralising.

Labelling

We label others and ourselves when we make global statements based on behaviour in specific situations. We might use this label even though there are many more examples that aren't consistent with that label.

Emotional reasoning

This thinking style involves basing your view of situations or yourself on the way you are feeling. For example, the only evidence that something bad is going to happen is that you feel like something bad is going to happen.

Magnification and minimisation

In this thinking style, you magnify the positive attributes of other people and minimise your own positive attributes. It's as though you're explaining away your own positive characteristics.

So, you can see where your general thinking style fits in from the descriptions above. I myself use a lot of mind-reading. Identifying that I have a tendency to mind-read, and noticing when I do it, stops my unhelpful thinking in its tracks. I can tell myself that I can't read people's minds and that I don't know what the future will bring.

We all have a style of thinking. We all have automatic thoughts that pop into our heads, whether we invite them or not. Sometimes they are helpful and can make us feel good, other times they are unhelpful and make us feel bad. Generally we are able to shake off these unhelpful thoughts and carry on, for example if someone pushes past us or jumps a queue, we might feel an initial buzz of annoyance but we tend to let it pass. We don't tend to hold on to these thoughts for very long and we certainly don't let them ruin our day. However, when it comes to our families, our children and sleep issues, things are very different. Because we are so closely connected and attached to the concept of being a good parent, when we try to get our babies to sleep and it doesn't happen we immediately use this as a stick to beat ourselves with. The negative, ugly unhelpful thoughts come in streams and they are a lot harder for us to dismiss so we carry them with us all day, and often for very much longer. As a result it ruins our day, our week or even longer. Its impact is huge.

I want to teach you to let go of these ugly unhelpful thoughts and untruths about your parenting style. You are already partway there because you have seen that it's not your job to put your baby to sleep; once you believe this you can begin to detach yourself from the feeling that the fact your baby is not sleeping at present is your fault. I want to teach you to let go of most if not all of those unhelpful thoughts that stop you from starting the sleep plan, or that try to get you to stop working on the plan. I want you to believe that you are doing the very best job, and that you are your own sleep consultant and baby charmer. I want you to believe that by working on your sleep plan, your baby will establish a healthy sleeping habit and you will all be successful. You need to believe this because your baby needs your helpful and balanced thinking in order to sleep. So we are going to use thoughts records to help us monitor our thinking and help us to change how we think so that we are in a better frame of mind to stay on track with our sleep plan. It's more than just simply thinking positively because sometimes being positive isn't truthful, sometimes being positive doesn't acknowledge the true nature of the situation and sometimes being positive doesn't validate the difficulty you may be experiencing. Sometimes being positive just isn't at all believable, so I want to introduce you to helpful thinking that replaces unhelpful styles.

Helpful thinking can be balanced, it can be truthful and it can be validating to you as a parent and a person who is struggling with your child's sleep. Examples of balanced helpful thoughts are:

'It may take me some time to get my baby to sleep but we will get there.'

'It's very hard to change my baby's sleep habits but if I remain consistent and follow the plan I can do it and my baby will sleep well.'

Prepare your thoughts record

Thoughts records are just one of the tools we psychologists use in CBT therapy to help our clients change their behaviour. It works by helping you to begin to notice the automatic thoughts that you have related to the area you want to change; in this situation it is sleep. By first noticing and then recording our thoughts we are able to see exactly how and what our barrier towards change is; once we know what it is, we can do something about it.

In our CBT model we want to replace the unhelpful thoughts with more helpful ones, so our thoughts record is a visual way of noting this down to remind ourselves on our journey of change what it is we have to do to break our vicious cycle. In essence, we are identifying unhelpful thoughts to challenge them with helpful thoughts and over time increase the number of automatic thoughts that are more balanced.

Let's begin by writing down the unhelpful thoughts you have in the table and space below. I have included my own example here to guide you.

Example of a thoughts record

Situation	Automatic unhelpful thought	Emotions	Balanced helpful thought	Emotions with balanced thought
Baby wakes in the middle of the night	I can't believe she's awake again. She will never sleep	Frustrated Sad	Her wakes at night are reducing. She is learning with our help to sleep better	Hopeful Determined

Notice the specific thoughts you have around your baby's sleep and the ones you have about your ability to change your child's sleeping habits. Often we don't actually mean what our automatic thoughts suggest; it's just our immediate reaction to a situation and not our considered, PAUSEd way of thinking. We normally have a thought that corresponds with how we feel and in a moment of frustration your automatic thought is of a negative nature.

But what would happen if you did PAUSE? What would happen if you could grab hold of that automatic negative thought, look at it carefully and ask it a few questions? What would happen if you were to look for the truth, the validity, the compassion of that negative automatic thought, and what would happen if you made a decision to reject it instead of accepting it and letting it ruin your day? What would happen if you were able to let go of that automatic negative thought and instead chose to hold and examine a new thought concept, a new way of thinking that felt more truthful, felt more validating and felt easier to sit with and sleep with?

Change your negative thoughts into helpful thoughts

It's important that we shape and change negative thoughts into balanced and helpful thoughts. You may find that your thoughts have a main theme running through them or that some can double up. If this is the case we can group them together and formulate one helpful and balanced thought that challenges it.

I want you to think about some statements that challenge your negative thoughts. Here are some questions you may wish to pose to your automatic thought that remains and continues to be an unhelpful intruder in your journey towards a healthy sleeping pattern:

What would someone else say about this situation?
What's the bigger picture?
Is there another way of seeing it?
What is the evidence that supports another way of viewing this?
Is this fact, feeling or opinion?
What advice would I give someone else?
Is my reaction in proportion to the actual event?

Is this situation within my control?
Can I put this worry aside?
If there are things in my control, can I make an action plan?
Where can I focus my attention?

By answering these questions you are challenging the negative automatic thoughts. Do this each and every time you notice that they are rearing their unhelpful heads. You know when you're most likely to see them, at your trigger points, which for sleep is usually naptime and bedtime. Arm yourself with this list of questions and your thoughts record and challenge your negative automatic thoughts. Soon you will be a master at this and you won't need your thoughts record to prompt you, but keep your record with you while you are learning to challenge and let go of the unhelpful thought.

We now need to write down helpful thoughts, and these will form the basis of your new approach and outlook on the sleep situation. You have changed your view from worry about the sleep plan working to believing that you can do this and your baby will sleep. Looking again at the thoughts record on page 87, you will see I have included a column headed 'balanced helpful thought'. Below are some of the questions and instructions that helped me to come up with thoughts in that column:

What could I do differently? What would be more effective?
Do what works! Act wisely.
Is it within my control to do something about this situation?
What can I do now that would help this situation?
Can I do anything later? What? When?
What will be most helpful for me or the situation?
What can I do or think about that I can focus my attention on?

As I've said, we can change the way we think or look at something, but what builds our confidence and changes our belief is evidence. So the final step in monitoring and challenging our negative thoughts is to look for the evidence. What evidence supports or undermines your negative view? In most cases we can never find much evidence that supports the negative unhelpful thought and we usually find lots of evidence that supports the more balanced view. Being more skilful in your approach to changing your baby's sleeping habit will help you challenge your negative thoughts and unhelpful thinking style and lead you towards helpful thoughts and a positive way of thinking.

Questions for you

- What is going on at your child/ren's bedtime?
- What time does Daddy get home?
- What is Daddy's role at bedtime, if any?
- How has the advice you've received affected the way you view your parenting skills?
- How do you prepare your child for sleep?
- How are you/your partner feeling?
- How has your child/ren's sleeping habits affected you and your partner as a couple?
- What would you like to happen?
- What are the main issues for you?
- What other things are a priority in the home?
- Do you devote time to yourself to reflect and regroup?
- How confident are you in your parenting skills?
- How can you become more confident?
- What do you need to do to trust your own instincts?
- Is this a worry or a fact, what is the evidence?

The answers to these questions will provide you with your sleeping plan action points and highlight what you need to do. For example, knowing what your priorities are means you can make adjustments to your lifestyle if it doesn't fit in with helping your family gain natural sleep patterns. By identifying and defining each family member's role you are each taking a piece of the plan and working together to overcome the sleep problem as a family.

You already have nearly all the key elements to build your plan. We will now talk about how mindfully you can put your plan into action and use all the knowledge you have gained from my coaching towards natural sleep success. Let's take an in-depth look at how one family works.

CASE STUDY

Background

Kate is a mother of twin girls and stays at home to raise them; her partner Joan works full time and travels frequently. Neither of the mothers' families lives nearby, so the lion's share of the care for the twins rests with Kate when Joan is away. Kate came to my clinic as she was having problems with Adel's sleeping habits and Rachel's use of the dummy, although Rachel slept well and rarely woke at night.

The twins, aged 10 months, are happy, social and engaging. They are on mixed feeds and enjoy lots of time with their mother, Kate. They attend groups, go on outings during the day and would often come home at varied times. Kate wants her children to experience a variety of things and interact with other children. It is also an opportunity for Kate to have contact with other adults and so she schedules activities for every day.

The twins share a room next door to their mothers and are in separate cots that are side by side. Both parents wish for the girls to continue to share a room but are concerned that Adel's frequent wakes will disturb Rachel and so they attend to Adel as soon as she wakes and Kate is breastfeeding her. Kate also feeds Adel to sleep as she has found that this is the quickest and easiest way to get her to sleep without tears. Kate also checks in on Rachel when she feeds Adel and if she notices that the dummy has fallen out she will put it back in Rachel's mouth as a measure to keep her calm and asleep. Kate has stated that she cannot bear to hear her daughters cry and that the crying makes her feel awful and triggers memories of her upbringing that she does not want her children to experience. She acknowledges that she gives her babies whatever they need as long as it stops them from crying and being distressed.

Adel

Adel is a very active and somewhat restless baby. She is engaging, a good eater, enjoys being cuddled by her mothers and breastfeeds at regular intervals throughout the day and night. She is happy to have a feed before a nap and once she is down she can sleep for 40 minutes. At night-time she is settled again by her mother and falls asleep on the breast. Once she is in the cot she will sleep for two hours before her first wake. She will require a feed and then settles again; however, she will wake every one to two hours and may cry or stir and moan and require the breast to get back off to sleep at night. While Adel is generally a happy baby she does cry and become distressed if she is not offered the breast.

Rachel

Rachel is an easy-going baby and is as content to be cuddled as she is to be sitting on her own playing. She accepts both the bottle and breast. She is not dependent on the breast or the bottle to fall asleep during the day or night but will accept a dummy. Once she is placed in her cot she will suck on her dummy until she falls asleep. Rachel will occasionally wake during the night but rarely more than once and she is easily soothed by placing the dummy in her mouth.

Problem

I assessed the sleep problem as being one of dependency, where Adel is so used to going to sleep on the breast that she has learnt that the only way she can fall asleep is by being held by her mother and fed to sleep. As Adel is placed in her cot once she is asleep she is not aware of her environment or familiar with it. She has not had the opportunity to develop other ways to fall asleep with her mother or by herself, and therefore becomes confused in the middle of the night when she wakes up and realises that her mother is not there. This confusion turns to distress as she is tired and wants to sleep but needs her mother to hold and feed her in order to do so.

Adel's distress and crying are too upsetting for Kate to bear, so she immediately meets her daughter's needs and offers the breast as comfort. This action serves to calm Adel back to sleep; however, her sleep problem is maintained as the only way she can be comforted and go back to sleep is by breastfeeding. Kate's actions are led by fear and anxiety. These strong emotional urges lead Kate to always react as soon as her daughter stirs, anticipating the distress before it happens. Kate is also fearful that Adel's cries will wake her sister and therefore she ensures that she always gets to Adel prior to her starting to cry.

Kate's style of parenting is permissive *(see page 119)* *and during the day she meets her children's needs to ensure they do not cry. Therefore, she spends a lot of time and energy attempting to calm and keep her babies happy. As her children's main caretaker, this results in her being physically exhausted. By avoiding hearing her daughters' cries, Kate not only misses the opportunity to learn the different kinds of cries her babies have, but also the opportunity to find out how best to meet their needs in the long term and use and exercise 'skills muscles' other than the breast.*

Kate shared her negative automatic thoughts with me and these were noted as: 'Adel needs the breast to sleep', 'breast is the quickest and easiest way to calm Adel', 'hearing my daughters cry wrecks me'.

Kate's vicious cycle

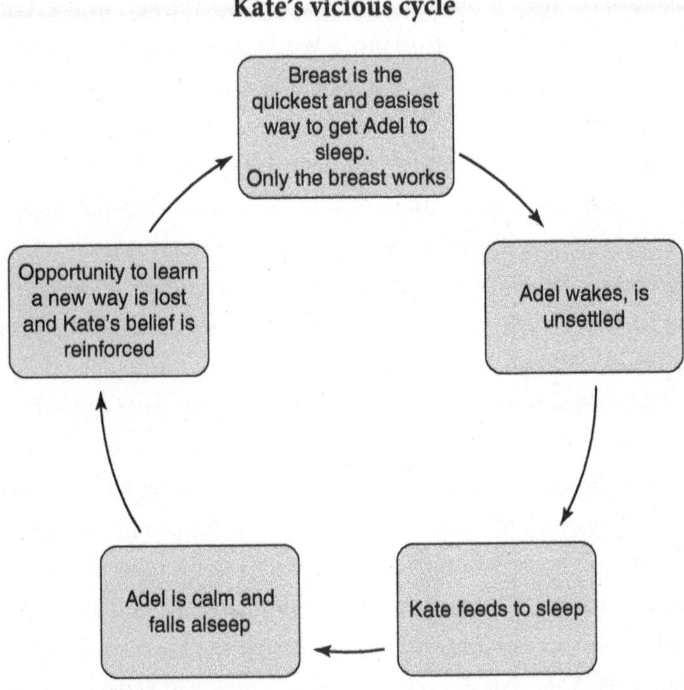

Plan

Action point 1

I advised Kate to spend one week of learning and practising working on mindfulness strategies to manage her emotions and anxieties. In order to not be led by her fear of her children crying, Kate needs to practise mindfulness techniques twice daily in order to help concentrate on the here and now, and train her brain to not fast forward to worries about the future but remain focused on achieving her goals. These goals are for her to remain calm and to work on teaching Adel to be soothed by means other than the breast.

In addition, Kate should spend one week challenging negative automatic thoughts and replacing them with helpful thoughts such as: 'I can soothe my daughters', 'breastfeeding is only one way that can calm and help Adel to sleep', 'I can teach Adel to accept soothing in another way'.

Action point 2

For four days, Kate needs to work on changing the way she interacts with her daughters during the day. She needs to use different levels of intervention so that she is able to hear her daughters' crying language and decipher what they need. In addition, she is to practise different levels of intervention and increase the time between each step. This is so that Adel learns that she can be soothed in other ways. Kate is to breastfeed only when Adel is hungry; at all other times in the day, Kate should settle Adel using the levels of intervention and grading up and down accordingly. This will teach Adel that she can be soothed by other methods and show Kate evidence that touch, voice and presence as calming tools can be as effective as the breast.

Action point 3

This action point focuses on settling back to sleep. Kate is to bottle feed Rachel and place her in her cot with her dummy and then focus on Adel. Kate should also split breastfeeds for Adel: one short feed before the bath and one after. Ideally, this would be a naked feed and then Kate could dress Adel after the second feed. After the second feed, Kate should bring Adel into her room and cuddle her until she is calm. She should then place Adel in her cot leaving her to fall asleep. Kate should use levels of intervention inside the cot, should Adel need calming. Kate is advised not to breastfeed outside of feeding times and that her 10pm feed should be pre-emptive.

Kate is allowed to get into the cot with Adel, or sleep with her by her side. Kate chose to get into the cot. This was done for the first two nights of the plan. This reduces distress and is a nice bridge away from breastfeeding, and allows Kate and Adel to be close.

On the third night of the plan, Kate will split feed, place Adel in her cot and calm her from outside the cot. Kate needs to avoid using PU/PD as Adel is too old and this would be too disruptive to the settling process. As Adel has spent the last four days learning how to be settled differently, by this time she knows that this is her and her mother's new routine. As a result, she will be more accepting and therefore her distress in the night-time settling will be significantly reduced. Should Adel become upset, and this is noted by a constant cry without waves, then Kate can use her top-level intervention of picking up, but only twice in the settling process. Once calm Adel is placed back into her cot and she falls asleep. For now, the night-time wakes should be managed in the same way as they were prior to this plan.

Action point 4

Kate should be mindful about giving Rachel the dummy when she does not need it, and she should only be given the dummy as a means of settling her at night. Kate needs to focus on Adel and allow Rachel to get used to Adel's grumbles and become desensitised to the disruption.

Action point 5

On day 4, the focus should be on the night-time settling and wakes at night. Wakes at night should all be managed by different levels of intervention, except feeds that are structured at 10pm, an optional feed at 2am and 6am Kate needs to allow Adel a couple of minutes of grumbling and frustration to give her the opportunity to resettle herself, but is to remain in the room until Adel and Rachel are both sleep. Kate should also continue using mindfulness and challenging her negative thoughts throughout the duration of the plan.

Action point 6

Kate should monitor and review progress through the use of both a thoughts record and sleep record.

Action point 7

At week 2, Kate should place Adel in her cot after her feed and read stories to both girls. Once they are calm and happy to have each other as company Kate can leave the room and check them periodically before they call out.

Outcome

Kate valued having a structure and a plan to follow and she enjoyed our on-going telephone consultations, which meant she felt support where she didn't before. Kate was able to use the mindfulness strategies straight away and noticed above all the calming effects it had on her. She struggled to bring her mind back from the behaviour she had learnt in childhood and mindfulness was the one skill she needed most. Kate persevered and along with challenging her initial negative automatic thoughts and staying in the moment, she noticed that interacting with her daughter in the day was easier and she felt much happier. Kate also noticed that the twins were good company for each other and that there were times when she did not need to do very much other than just be present. She was able to successfully use the different levels of intervention in the day and it came as a big surprise that Adel responded very well to this. Kate was also pleasantly surprised that her breastfeeding in the day reduced. As a result she spent quality time with the girls and had more energy.

Importantly, seeing this change gave Kate all the evidence she needed and the confidence to start to change things in the night. Adel responded to the split-feeding well and remained awake when lying down. In the first two nights, she fell asleep in her mother's arms without issue, though it did take a longer time than normal. On the third and fourth night, she was a little unhappy and Kate had to reassure her using the resettling techniques. By the end of the week Adel was settling in her cot and falling asleep independently. Rachel used the dummy at night and didn't really need it in during the day. She woke on occasion when Adel was upset but she remained calm and chatty in the cot and would go back to sleep.

It took Kate three weeks to reduce the night wakes for Adel and she achieved this by following the plan of levels of intervention and allowing Adel to become frustrated and resettle herself. At the end of the six-week plan Adel would only sometimes wake for her 10pm dream feed but settled back to sleep afterwards. She no longer wakes in the night.

Chapter 5

Mindful Ways Towards Sleep

Did you know: Mindfulness meditation can help people reduce stress and fall asleep?

SLEEP IS ON YOUR MIND, YOU ARE CONSUMED BY THE THOUGHT of sleep, you spend your whole day focused on sleep: the trouble is neither you nor your child are getting any at the moment. The more you focus on sleep the worse it seems to feel. How do you unlock this vicious cycle?

Mindfulness is the skill, the practice and the answer. I will talk about how the use of mindfulness can help you manage your emotions, your feelings, so that they don't become a hindrance when you are trying to shape your baby's behaviour. Mindfulness is one of the five areas that are on your sleep formulation for you to fill in and will form your own unique sleep plan. Before you begin to work on your child's sleep and improve the quality of your own, you need to be in the right state of mind. For this, I need you to learn and practise a new skill: mindfulness.

What is mindfulness?

Mindfulness is a way of deliberately and non-judgementally focusing your attention on what is happening right in the moment, whether that is your emotions, body sensations and/or thoughts. Holding this book, focusing on the words and the feeling of your body resting in a chair is an example of mindfulness. This skill is derived from the Buddhist practice of meditation, but it has become popular today in the Western world. Mindfulness has successfully been used to promote well-being, increase concentration and improve physical health.

Mindfulness in practice is a way of attending to the present experience, good or bad, without interpretation. This non-judgemental approach to your life helps to reduce and limit stress, distress and the impact of negative emotions. There are many ways we can practise mindfulness, through doing or participating, observing, visualisation or writing.

How I use mindfulness in my work, and how you will now learn to use it, is a generic approach to noticing what you are doing and how you are doing it, engaging all your five senses: sight, sound, touch, taste and smell. We will do this to ensure we are in the right emotional state to soothe our babies; this will help you limit and restrict negative automatic thoughts that get in the way of you being successful on your sleep plan.

You are probably all too familiar with a new baby's 'witching hour' between 4pm and 7pm; this time of the day is the perfect opportunity to introduce mindfulness techniques to help you get through this difficult period.

When I was trying to get my twin daughters to sleep through the night, I had a choice – I could focus on all the other things that needed to be done in and around the home, the washing, the cooking, the cleaning, the other children, not to mention finding time to eat and take care of myself. But I had to get the twins to sleep and in order to do this I had to focus. I had to put all my attention to the task of sleep. If I didn't then the twins would not sleep and I would feel deflated. I had to remain mindful and stay in the moment, the here and now, controlling my mind, my emotions and my behaviour. Sophie and Charlotte began to sleep through the night because I was first able to attend to the task at hand; I was not distracted or motivated by fear. I was successful because I broke the unhelpful thought cycle and controlled my state by staying mindful. I was able to focus on one child at a time, I was able to use mindfulness to calm my fears and regulate my heartbeat so that I was in the right position to help my babies sleep by feeling calm and relaxed, because I was calm and relaxed.

A lot of the emotional distress that we experience is related to us thinking about upsetting things that have happened in the past (not being able to get your baby to sleep is a prime example) or anticipating events that may or may not happen in the future. These thoughts, past and present, cause us to experience negative and unwelcome emotions. Mindfulness is about the present, and negative feelings such as anger, anxiety, guilt and sadness become much easier to handle if we focus on the here and now, taking each moment as it comes. I use mindfulness at every opportunity: when I notice I am feeling emotional or unfocused, I mindfully drink tea, take a bath, smell a flower, whatever it takes to change my state – you get the idea.

Why is being mindful so important? Well, children can pick up on your emotional state – if you are tense and upset then so will your child be; if you're distracted you can't focus and your efforts lose power and effectiveness. By being mindful you are making your first step towards change.

Practise mindfulness every day to build your mastery at it. Above all else, practise the two most important skills: noticing your breathing and letting go. The breathing exercise below is a good way of helping you focus and relax which you will need when things get a little tricky during your sleep plan journey, and the letting-go exercise on page 104 is useful for being able to turn your mind away from unpleasant thoughts that cause you distress. When you practise these examples of mindfulness, make sure that you are in a safe place where you can be quiet, close your eyes and focus.

Breathing exercise

This is an exercise to increase your mindfulness of the present moment so that you can clear away thoughts about past and future events. Notice each thought, try not to suppress it or interpret it, just notice your thoughts as if they were signs you were passing by. These thoughts are just thoughts and cannot harm you. Don't try to control the thought, just accept the thoughts coming and going as natural events in your mind, neutral events that will come and go. It is normal for you to experience intrusive thoughts and your attention will drift from time to time. Don't worry – the art of mindfulness is the skill in being able to notice that your attention has drifted away and being able to bring your mind back to the task.

* Start by focusing on your breathing.
* Breathe in through your nose and slowly out through your mouth as if blowing through a straw.
* Just notice the air moving into and out of your body. Notice the breath as it enters your nostrils and as it passes through your lips.
* If thoughts enter your mind, notice them, label them as just thoughts and then gently bring your attention back to your breath leaving and entering your body; focus your attention only on your breathing.

* Notice the sensations of breathing air in.
* Notice the sensations of breathing air out.
* As you breathe air into your body, say the phrase and think 'Just this one breath in'.
* As you breathe air out of your body, say the phrase and think 'Just this one exhale out'.
* Just this one breath in.
* Just this one exhale out.
* Just this one breath.
* Just this one exhale.
* Keep repeating this for a few moments.
* Continue focusing only on each breath in and each breath out, and when you notice your attention drifting, as it will do naturally from time to time, just gently bring your attention back to noticing your breath, stay in the moment; try not to anticipate your next movement or even your next breath. Only focus on one breath at a time.
* Continue focusing on each breath in and each exhale for 2–3 minutes.

In this exercise we focused on the breath, which is called an anchor – an anchor to hold our attention to – and then we attached a mantra (the repeated phrase of the in breath and the out breath), to help us focus. The focus on the breath is a powerful awareness activity as it has the advantage of helping you focus your attention on the whole body; importantly it focuses your attention to the function – breathing – that is both consciously and unconsciously controlled.

Here you are practising the skill of being able to let events happen without control and with acceptance. We cannot control our thoughts, we can only choose to let them come and go and not be emotionally driven by them. We let out the breath without trying to control it, we just let it be, just as we want to do with our thoughts. Focusing on breathing helps you practise focusing your mind without trying to control or interpret your thoughts, as breath is a neutral event that happens whether we think about it or not. When you can treat your negative thoughts in the same way as your breath, you know you have mastered the art of mindfully letting go.

Letting-go exercise

This is an exercise to increase your mindfulness of the present moment so that you can clear away thoughts about past and future events and practise the art of letting go.

Some of our distress is caused by our attachment to ideas, thoughts, concepts, people and things. Buddhists believe that by letting go of attachments we can reduce our suffering. We are social creatures and therefore attachment is important to us. But what we can do is let go of our attachment to things such as unhelpful thoughts and the emotions that are associated with them in order to limit our pain and stress.

* Start by observing your breathing. You may have your eyes open or closed but sometimes it's easier to visualise when you have your eyes closed as you reduce the visual distraction.
* Don't try to change anything about your breathing, just notice the sensations of breathing air into and out of your body.
* As you close your eyes I want you to imagine that you are sitting beside a stream, with water gently flowing over rocks and rippling past you, and a tree full of leaves. As you imagine this I want you to notice how this makes you feel.
* Let your mind focus on the water in the stream and notice how clear it is. Notice the colours, the texture and smell. Notice the leaves on the tree and notice each leaf as it floats from the tree and into the stream.

* If any thoughts drift into your mind, imagine yourself breathing them out so that each thought flows downstream, like leaves on the current. Each leaf that falls from the tree represents a thought that has entered your mind. Try not to interpret the thoughts, they are just thoughts that, like the leaves, float away and down into the stream.
* Allow your thoughts to drift away from you until your mind focuses just on the image of letting go of each thought as it enters your mind, moment by moment – only filled by the image of crystal clear water. Notice how letting go feels, notice the leaves as they gently flow downstream away and out of view. These leaves gently go away and all that is left are the feel and sound of the water from the stream.
* Continue with this imagery for 2–3 minutes.

By the practice of mindfulness you will become more and more aware of the full and colourful range of your experiences. Like your baby, you will become more sensitive to your own senses, your urges and your impulses. The more skilful you become you will be aware of your own quality of your mindfulness and understand your mind being busy, clear, calm, agitated or foggy.

The non-judgemental stance is key in mindfulness and the reduction in distress because you are not trying to appraise the content of your thoughts. This will allow you to become freer to observe your thoughts without spending too much time analysing what your thought might mean: you can just let it go. Just like the stream and leaves exercise above you can allow the thoughts to come as streams and let them go without holding on to them for any length of time. You are building in your own protection against your thoughts so that you reduce your stress, and all of this will help you remain calm, help keep your baby calm, and ultimately help your baby sleep.

Practising mindfulness

Environment and posture

You can practise the art of mindfulness anywhere, but some visualisations are more suited to quiet conditions. I would advise all beginners to start off practising mindfulness in a quiet place where you will have little to no distractions. You may be familiar with the meditation where people sit with their legs crossed on the floor. However, this is not a prerequisite for mindfulness; in fact, you can mindfully drink a cup of tea, paint your toenails and even have a bath (if you have time!) Mindfulness is about being able to focus on the present and so enjoy any activity that will allow you to do that. Doing one thing at a time will be good practice at being non-judgemental, mindful and distress free.

Eyes open or closed

There is an argument that as we live our lives with our eyes open, we must learn to be mindful with our eyes open. However, it takes a well-practised person to be able to stay focused when there are so many visual and auditory distractions around us. When you are just learning to be mindful it will help to close your eyes. When you are ready to expand your mindfulness practice you may like to practise being mindful with your eyes open.

Be non-judgemental

During your mindfulness practice you are aiming to address your thoughts and images as being equal, no matter the intensity or the content. By doing this you are practising being non-judgemental, which is at the core of mindfulness. Label the thoughts as just thoughts, as we have just practised.

Deal with distractions

During the exercises above I talked to you about being distracted. We know that the more you try to suppress a thought the more you think of it, so mindfulness is about learning how to manage your distractions and bring your focus back to the present moment. Thought streams are natural and, without beating yourself up for having lost your focus, just notice that you have wandered off the path and again gently bring your attention focus back. We are trying to break a habit we have learnt over many years – to become distracted by our thoughts as the urge and the emotional pull can sometimes be so strong – but as we practise seeing thoughts as just thoughts we take the urgency and emotional sting out of the thought stream and we can let go, bringing our attention back to the present. We are moving in and out of the thought stream, bringing our attention back to what is important.

Other external factors can distract us too, such as sounds, people, noise, aches and pains in our body. Do the same… notice and then bring your attention back. Strong emotions can sometimes be problematic but again try not to interpret or judge the emotion. Instead, be curious about the sensation, notice it and view it as just an event that is trying to distract you rather than overwhelm you.

You will notice before you go to tend to your baby's need and while you are in the room that practising mindfulness will help you to stay on track and stay focused on your goal. Repeat your mantra and stay in the moment doing one thing at a time, not being distracted by emotions, noise, sensations or past events, knowing that by being mindful and non-judgemental you will be more successful.

Using mindfulness as part of your sleep plan

When we start turning past events over and over in our minds it makes us feel low and, in extreme cases, depressed. These events cannot be changed, we cannot do anything about them but they affect how we feel right now, for example, thinking 'My child has always slept badly, all the things I have tried before have never worked.' The more we think back to how bad the sleeping has been the worse we feel, putting us into a vicious cycle.

When we start to think about the future or we fast forward to weeks and months ahead, this makes us feel anxious. We have thoughts such as, 'What if she doesn't sleep tonight, what if she never sleeps ever, what will happen to us as a family two or three weeks from now?' The more these worries about the future enter our mind the more anxious we become.

Mindfulness teaches us to think in the now, not to think in the past or too far into the future, therefore helping us not to feel low and not to feel anxious. It teaches us to stay in the moment: right now you have a good opportunity to change your experience, right now you have a good opportunity to learn and a good opportunity to teach your baby to sleep. Today, right now, is what is in my focus, in my view and in my control. Mindfulness is about the present and our emotions are managed because our thoughts are not in the past or the future, but in the very moment.

When you notice your mood change and you feel low or anxious you may be able to PAUSE and this will turn things around. But sometimes we have travelled too far down the road of worry and anxiety and we may find it hard to bring our attention back to the present. In times like these, you are best trying to ride that wave of low mood and anxiety, give yourself space and give your baby space. The feelings will pass but until then accept the feelings and know these two things: you can cope, and these feelings will rise and fall. Allow and accept your mood to rise and fall, and try not to act on these feelings when you notice them as these are the negative emotions that will lead you to undesired behaviour, such as taking your baby out of the room, rocking/feeding to sleep or, worse still, giving up. By staying focused you stand a better chance of meeting your baby's needs and helping them to sleep because you have managed your emotions and have not been led by intrusive thoughts and worries about past or future events.

As we become masters at mindfully being aware of our situation and practising the skills of letting go, focusing and becoming non-judgemental, we notice that our emotions are not as intense and this puts us in an excellent position to make the changes we need to ensure natural sleep for our babies. Mindfulness is not only a way to solve your problems but it is also a way for you and your family to connect. Being mindful teaches us to appreciate the moment we are experiencing and by doing this we start to appreciate and notice our families and ourselves more. The next chapter looks at you and your family and how sleep impacts on you all.

Chapter 6

Why your child's sleep is a family issue

Did you know: Getting to know how sleep impacts on the family is vital?

WHEN I GET A PHONE CALL OR AN EMAIL FROM DESPERATE parents, they almost always start with talking about their child's sleep and request help for that child. This seems logical but the unspoken cry for help is usually that the whole family is having problems sleeping. It would be so easy to focus on the child and just the child alone, but if I did this I would be doing my clients a disservice. My approach is inclusive, not exclusive. Sleep is a whole family issue and as such you need a plan that is going to work for your child, you and everyone else in the household. So whenever I speak to parents I ask them what they want, what will work for them and, most importantly, how this has affected them, not only sleepwise, but emotionally, and how it has affected their relations with other people they care about. I also look at the family's health and mood as these are also important when thinking about how to help and make positive changes. You see, I am looking at a solution that not only lasts but benefits everyone and makes everyone feel as though their needs are just as important as the child who happens to not be sleeping at present. I have worked with parents who have not shared a bed together in years, fathers sleeping in the front room, mothers sleeping on the floor, siblings feeling confused. I have worked with families who have suffered in silence and the lack of sleep has led to an increase in the level of stress within the home, as well as an increase in illnesses such as colds and flu.

It is time now to work on each member of the family and take a good hard look at what it is you want, and how you are going to get there. It is not important what other families are doing, because other families are not you! What might work for them might not work for you and how they live their lives and what they find acceptable is individual and unique to them. I have worked with working families who wish for their children to go to bed at 8pm or 9pm as they want time with their children before they go to bed. That might send some parents reeling in horror at the lateness of the hour, but they don't need to worry as it's not their family. It is okay to have a routine and plan that suits your family. If parents who worked put their children to bed at 6–7pm each night they would miss out on a lot and each family has to identify what is the most important issue for the family. That's why a one-size-fits-all approach isn't the answer. Finding out what your underlying sleeping problem is, and knowing how you want your child to sleep, while also factoring in the needs of the whole family puts you in an excellent position to make long-lasting change. There is no right or wrong answer – it's what you choose to be the most important issue at hand and what you as parents can live with, accept and enjoy. You can get sleep and your child will sleep, but first you need to know what type of family home you want to create and then identify your goal based on the consequences of sleep deprivation and what you will no longer put up with.

If you are a mum who misses contact with her partner, a dad who longs to return to the family bed, parents who are tired of being irritable and unhappy, and siblings who are finding it hard to sleep, concentrate and engage in the day, I am talking to you. Your family is important, you are important and so learning how to get sleep for you and your family is important because it affects you all.

The Valued Living Questionnaire

With that in mind why don't we take a look at just how happy you are and how your current situation has impacted on your life. This is the quiz I use with my clients who want to know how their values compare to how they are really living their lives. This exercise is simple and effective and can have some surprising results. Take this test to gain clarity and some insight into the quality-of-life areas that are important to you and note down anything that may be a surprise.

Fill in Part 1 of the quiz and circle each question according to how important each area is to you. When you have answered all ten questions put the sheet to one side. We will come back to this later. Then go to Part 2 and answer the same ten questions but think about how consistent you are in behaving and doing the things that are important to you. Add the score up for Part 2 and write this down.

Self-Care Assessment Part 1

Below are areas of life that are valued by some people. This questionnaire will help clarify your own quality-of-life in each of these areas. One aspect of quality-of-life involves the importance you put on different areas of living. Rate the importance of each area (by circling a number) on a scale of 1–10. A '1' means that area is *not at all important*. A '10' means that area is *extremely important.* Not everyone will value all of these areas, or value all areas the same. Rate each area according to **your own personal sense of importance.**

Area	Not at all important	Extremely important
1) Family (other than marriage or parenting)	1 2 3 4 5	6 7 8 9 10
2) Marriage/couples/intimate relationships	1 2 3 4 5	6 7 8 9 10
3) Parenting	1 2 3 4 5	6 7 8 9 10
4) Friends/social life	1 2 3 4 5	6 7 8 9 10
5) Work	1 2 3 4 5	6 7 8 9 10
6) Education/training	1 2 3 4 5	6 7 8 9 10
7) Recreation/fun	1 2 3 4 5	6 7 8 9 10
8) Spirituality/meaning and purpose in life	1 2 3 4 5	6 7 8 9 10
9) Citizenship/Community life	1 2 3 4 5	6 7 8 9 10
10) Physical self-care (nutrition, exercise/movement, rest/sleep)	1 2 3 4 5	6 7 8 9 10

Reflection: *How do you feel about this? Are there any areas that surprised you?*

Self-Care Assessment Part 2

In this section, please give a rating of how **consistent** your actions have been with each of your values. Please note that this is **not** asking about your ideal in each area, **nor** what others think of you. Everyone does better in some areas than in others. People also do better at some times than at others. Please just indicate how you think you have been doing during the past week. Rate each area (by circling a number) on a scale of 1–10. A '1' means that your actions have been *not at all consistent with your value.* A '10' means that your actions have been *completely consistent with your value.*

During the past week...

Area	Not at all consistent with my value					Completely consistent with my value				
1) Family (other than marriage or parenting)	1	2	3	4	5	6	7	8	9	10
2) Marriage/couples/intimate relationships	1	2	3	4	5	6	7	8	9	10
3) Parenting	1	2	3	4	5	6	7	8	9	10
4) Friends/social life	1	2	3	4	5	6	7	8	9	10
5) Work	1	2	3	4	5	6	7	8	9	10
6) Education/training	1	2	3	4	5	6	7	8	9	10
7) Recreation/fun	1	2	3	4	5	6	7	8	9	10
8) Spirituality/meaning and purpose in life	1	2	3	4	5	6	7	8	9	10
9) Citizenship/Community life	1	2	3	4	5	6	7	8	9	10
10) Physical self-care (nutrition, exercise/movement, rest/sleep)	1	2	3	4	5	6	7	8	9	10
Total: ______________										

Now take a look at both sheets and compare your answers. What do you notice? Are you living a life that is consistent with your value of importance? Look at your scores for Part 2: 10 is the minimum and 100 is the maximum. The higher the number the more likely you are to experience contentment in your life. No matter what you have scored, this questionnaire will have given you some insight into your values and whether you are contented.

During this journey towards sleep you should hope to maintain your high score or improve on your overall score. By helping you gain sleep for you and your family we can at least improve a few areas of your life that are important to you and increase your overall happiness. Take Part 2 of this test again at the end of implementing your plan successfully and once you have had good sleep for at least a week, compare your scores and see again what you notice.

Define your role

In my experience, I've observed that in most families there is one parent responsible for the lion's share of the caregiving. The other is responsible for the other important tasks that make the family run smoothly, such as financial planning, shopping, and house maintenance. In this day and age we are less constrained by traditional roles and expectations, and instead focus on what works. Each family is unique, amazing and full of colour. Some families may feel very comfortable with their members taking on the traditional roles while others may find that for them this cap just does not fit.

This is the main reason I believe that the route to success is defining what your role is in your family. If you are in a position to know what your responsibilities are, and those of each member of the family, this is a sure-fire way of reducing stress and eliminating anxiety. You are on the road to success when you know what is expected of you and what others will deliver. This way you avoid disappointment and the responsibility of running and maintaining home life is shared. You are empowered because not only do you realise what is within your job description but also what isn't, and you can push back on that without guilt. You not only manage your expectations but those of others and it makes for a seamless and frustration-free household. It doesn't matter how you choose to divide the chores in your home; as long as each one has a member of the family assigned to it, you will all pull together and get the job done. So if parents decide to take alternate nights to resettle the baby, you know when it's not your night you can damn well sleep and let the other parent do their job.

Before you embark on any journey to change sleeping patterns, ensure you are clear about what your role is, be clear what the role is of each family member and get a commitment from them that they will hold up their end of the bargain. If you give your other children jobs to do at bedtime, like reading a story to the baby, then get their agreement and reward them for continued effort with charts and verbal praise For this to work it's important that each family member is happy in their role, is in the right mood and agrees to do the tasks assigned to them. If not, then your family members will be unhappy at best and resentful at worst. You don't want this, least of all because it's not fair on you and it won't make you a happy bunny in the process. This is also a very quick way to make your sleep plan fail before you have even begun. You need to agree with your family the roles you will all play to make the next few weeks of sleep training a complete success. For example, one of my families gave the children the job of packing away after dinner and bringing the laundry down from all the bedrooms: this was done while Mum focused on putting the baby down. Dad's role was to oversee that the tasks were being completed by the older children and get them off to bed once they had finished. These tasks were well defined and had been agreed upon by all family members, which meant that implementing the sleep plan was quick and successful. The quicker you agree the quicker and closer you are to your natural sleep pattern through nurturing becoming a reality.

Share the responsibility

Consistency can sometimes feel like taking one step forward and two steps back. It can seem even harder to achieve if you have more than one person working on the sleep pattern. Sometimes you may think it's easier for just one person to do all the work, to ensure consistency. The problem with this approach, however, is that when you shoulder all of the work you are more likely to be inconsistent because you are tired, exhausted, confused and you will look for the quickest and easiest 'solution' that will get you back into bed and asleep. This solution may work in the short term but it's part of the vicious cycle, the maintenance cycle, and will keep your problem going.

We need to avoid anything that stops us in our tracks and moves us further away from our ultimate goal, which is having our babies sleep well. Therefore it is far better that you plan who does what (this goes back to our discussion on roles) and accept that you can't do it all, and nor should you, and allow others in to help you, even if they don't do it in the same way as you do. This is perfectly fine as doing things in a different way isn't going to upset the sleep plan. Consistency is sending the same message, not necessarily doing the same thing. This means that we can all embrace our 'dance' with our babies; Dad can bond with baby and establish his own dance as long as he is sending the same message, using the PAUSE method and different levels of responsiveness. You can relax because you know that everyone in your family is on the same page.

Understand your parenting style

We, as parents, shape our children's lives: how we behave and communicate, in fact, virtually everything we do has an impact on how our children develop, how they interact with the world and how they perceive it. So no pressure there! From the moment our children are born, we become their beacons for directing their lives and so it is entirely understandable why becoming a new parent is such an anxious time. A fellow psychologist, Diana

Baumrind, found through her naturalistic observational research ('Parenting Styles in Psychology', Brittany Olivarez) that we can all be roughly placed into four styles of parenting. Knowing what type of parenting style you fit into will help you decide on how helpful it is to change your child's sleeping behaviour. You may even wish to change your style of parenting based on what you are trying to achieve for your child, or you may wish to become more flexible in your parenting to match your child's temperament. All of these reasons are valid because we are embarking on a journey of 'doing what works' as opposed to what 'someone says is right'. You may be unaware that you even have a parenting style and so this journey will be of huge benefit to you. Knowledge is power and power gives you more choice. Remember that you can make positive changes that will affect the way your child sleeps for the better.

The authoritative parent

This is a democratic style of parenting where the parents are described as being attentive and forgiving. This style of parenting teaches children how to behave well and learn from experience within the safety of boundaries. Parents devise a set of rules, and if the child fails to follow those rules there are consequences that are used to stop the undesired behaviour. If the boundaries are followed, parents using this style will encourage the behaviour with reward.

The permissive parent

This style of parenting sees parents take on the role of 'friends' rather than parents. Conversely in this description parents have no or little expectations of their child, and as such they allow the children to make their own decisions.

> To be more successful, view setting boundaries as a firm cuddle that helps your baby feel safe and secure.

The authoritarian parent

These parents will have high expectations of their children but with very little communication between child and parents. These parents frequently fail to provide logical reasoning for rules and limits, and are prone to administer harsh punishments for childhood indiscretions.

> Being able to be flexible, communicating effectively and adjusting to your child's temperament will mean you are more likely to have a plan and routine that fits in with your lifestyle.

The uninvolved parent

This style of parenting neglects the child. Parents using this style of parenting will quite often put their own life before the child's. They provide for the child's basic needs but they have little interaction with their children.

> By learning to read your children's behaviours and communicate with them you are able to shape their behaviour. This will mean that you have more free time and you will improve your mood. You will also have your needs met if your baby is sleeping in a natural pattern.

Each of these varying forms of parenting will impact and influence the development of a child both positively and negatively, depending on the style chosen. Interestingly, Baumrind found that well-balanced and socially appropriate children often came from family homes where the authoritative parenting style was implemented.

Most of us will use a combination of styles. This may be because we are co-parenting with another adult, sharing care as part of a blended family or living with extended family. The role each family member plays in shaping your child's behaviour – and more specifically sleeping behaviour – is crucial. Your style of parenting will affect your baby's sleep as it dictates how you respond to him. Our style of parenting affects how our child feels and how he responds to us and views his world. The way we communicate with our children is the cornerstone of their development, which means for successful entry into well-adapted adults, how we parent is fundamental. My advice is to try to adopt a parenting style that closely matches that of the authoritative style as this will ensure you are most successful on my naturally nurturing gentle sleep solution.

Understand your baby's temperament

We now need to address what it is that has led you to want to make a change: the baby who is currently not sleeping in the way you would like. Our babies didn't come with a written manual or even a quick guide to knowing how to meet his needs. So the job of discovering the manual within each baby falls to us. The good news is that as a parent you are the perfect person for the job; spending such a huge amount of time with your baby means that you are the expert on your child. This is where acknowledging your style of parenting and taking the steps to make changes within yourself, defining the key roles of your family members and having a clear focus on your goals, come into their own. The next step is to know what type of temperament your baby has and then match that to how you are or will be as a parent. Parents of newborns needn't worry, your baby's cries and their body language will be the best way you can be informed of their temperament, which we will discuss later.

While it is true that we all fall into patterns of behaviour, close observation can place our children's temperaments into three main groups. Studies have shown that for 60 per cent of children this will mean that they are more likely to behave in certain ways consistently. So let's describe the three main types with examples and you can then assess for yourself where your baby and/or children fit best.

The flexible child

You pretty much know where you are with this child as she eats, sleeps and poos in a regular fashion, and will follow a plan and a routine. She is able to easily adapt to all types of situations and environments with little frustration or fuss. These social creatures are happy to adjust to change and are a delight to interact with as they smile often. My clients usually tell me that their flexible child is always engaging, interested and curious. These babies have consistent moods that are related to their environment; while usually happy they will display the full range of emotions in an appropriate fashion. These babies will offer no resistance to sleep training and are ready and able to learn new things quickly and with little distress. This flexible child will match and suit most parenting styles; although I should hasten to add the most effective parenting style for this child would be authoritative.

The wilful/spirited child

This baby will have a very irregular eating, sleeping and pooing schedule and this will be difficult for those parents who are organised and like structure. These babies will be more rigid in their approach to new things and often show less positive emotions when placed in new situations. Parents of wilful babies tell me that they spend a lot of time reacting to things by crying or throwing tantrums. This usually is a sign of being unsettled and an inability to communicate how they are feeling. They are sensitive in that their moods shift frequently and they are more comfortable taking their time to familiarise themselves with their environment. These babes do not like to be pushed to take part in new situations and if faced with this scenario they will react in an oppositional way. These babies need time to change their sleeping habits, and parents will need to take on a more laid-back approach to allow this type of baby time to adjust to any changes with as little distress as possible. A strict style of parenting with this child will make for a very strained and difficult situation for all.

The cautious/wary child

This type of baby is often referred to as the slow-to-warm-up child. This child will often show signs of shyness and mild anxiety when entering new situations. However, over time and with familiarity these babies begin to relax and accept their new surroundings. My clients are keen to point out that these babies are able to fit into both an eating and sleeping routine. They tend to feel most comfortable when with their main caregiver and sleep issues may focus around needing to sleep with a parent or have the parent holding their hand in order to fall asleep. These children's moods are often dictated by their surroundings and can change frequently, so they can show signs of wilfulness and distress if they are made to do things they do not want to. They may act withdrawn or clingy, or refuse to move if placed in a new environment. These children may have difficulty with night wake-ups and need frequent reassurance from their parent in order to get to sleep.

Carey (1974) noted that children with low sensory thresholds were more likely to awaken at night, and that 'maternal anxiety, anger, and feelings of helplessness' may result from, rather than be caused by, the child's sleep problems. What Carey is suggesting here is that it is the child's low tolerance for stimulation that causes parents to became anxious and feel helpless rather than the sleep disturbance itself. By working on behaviours that underlie the sleep problem with the child's temperament you could improve sleep and thus improve the mother's situation.

CASE STUDY

Background

Jo and Andy are parents to Mary who was born with hearing impairments. They came to my sleep clinic wanting to learn how to manage and maintain a good healthy sleeping pattern given her special situation. Mary, who is 11 months old, sleeps in her own room and is bottle-fed. Mary has been a poor sleeper from birth, which was mainly due to many ear infections. As a result, her parents have struggled to get her into a sleeping pattern that allows her to sleep from when they put her to bed at 8pm until they wake at 7am Mary always goes to sleep with little problem and can, at times, manage to sleep for long periods. Mary wakes once or twice a night but when she does she stays awake for a long time and while she is awake she will begin making limited babbling sounds and playing. Most of the time Mary is calm and rarely cries, but will often stay awake and look around her world, keeping her brain active and alert and not in the necessary calm state for good healthy sleeping.

Jo and Andy are both loving and caring parents with a style of parenting that is more authoritarian. They were concerned that their baby was not in a proper structured routine. Furthermore, they were also concerned that not having a routine was essential if their daughter was to get the desired amount of sleep and remain healthy and well. Jo is a full-time mum and she cares for Mary's older sister who is aged 12 and sleeps well. Andy is a working father who often chooses to work from home at least once a week so that he can support Jo and the two children. Andy is a hands-on father and both Jo and he have worked out an arrangement whereby they equally share the chores and the care for the family's needs.

Mary

I assessed Mary as being a social, curious and active baby; she loves people and loves smiling. She has had many infections in her time, but has coped with them well and I did not assess her as having any fears associated with being put down as a result of pain association. However, what was noticeable was that her sleep was disturbed and she would stay awake for an hour or more at night. Mary loves her food and enjoys her milk at night. She is constantly looking around her and trying to make sense of her world through visual methods. Although Mary is not profoundly deaf, her hearing is limited to a degree that requires the family to respond to her in ways that help her to understand what is going on. Mary's room is a simple room in pastel white with all the necessary furniture and felt like a warm and calming room.

Problem

I assessed the problem as being a disturbed sleep cycle as a result of frequent disruptions in the night due to illness, feeding, and nappy changes. Her parents' involvement in order to care for Mary's special needs has meant that she has found it hard to establish a good and consistent sleeping pattern. Mary appears to be an easy baby, therefore I felt that she would cope well with changes made to her routine and this would bode well for the family as a whole.

Mary's parents' authoritative parenting style makes their current situation more of a problem for them as they find it hard to manage Mary's wakes and struggle to know what to do when she does wake. Additionally, Mary's special needs means that in order to support her sleeping pattern we have to use attachment-style tools that work to her advantage and ones she can respond well to.

Plan

My plan was to work with Jo and Andy on accepting a more relaxed and flexible approach to sleeping habits through what we in the field of behavioural psychology call 'psycho-education'. This is simply explaining the rationale on sleeping habits and understanding that a routine is just a small part of the process. My plan was to help them use different levels of interventions to soothe and respond to Mary at night.

Mary's problem is not related to an association or dependency as she is able to go down to sleep well at night and, at times, is able to sleep for long periods. As there is no pattern to Mary's wakes, I assessed that working on joining up Mary's body rhythm would be the focus, in addition to teaching Mary's parents how best to tailor her environment to ensure it worked well at keeping her calm and helping her back off to sleep. The next stage was then to support the parents on being able to respond well to Mary at night, in a consistent fashion that would promote good healthy sleeping using different levels of responsiveness and gradual retreat to join up the sleep cycle.

Mary's vicious sleep cycle

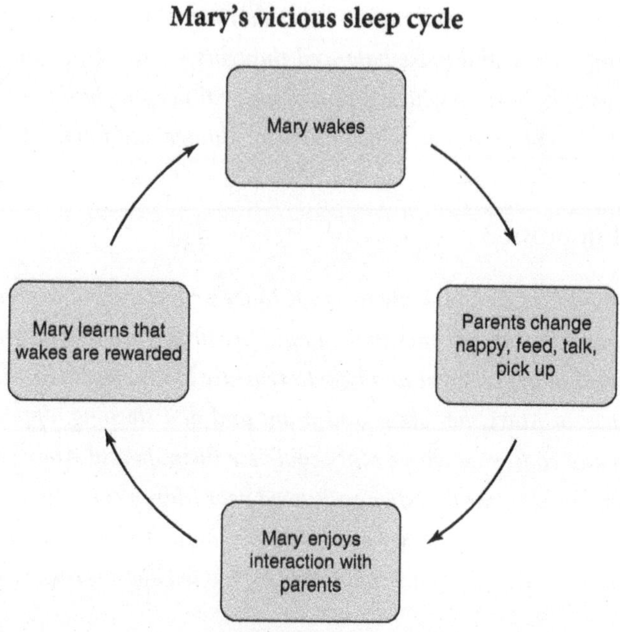

Action point 1

I talked through sleep psycho-education with Mary's parents. I explained that having a sequence of events to follow once they came home was a more flexible routine to adopt. Mary has a disrupted sleep cycle and has learnt to stay awake and alert as she is waiting for her parents to attend to her – something that she can only do by sight. This sends the message to her body circadic rhythm that it is okay to wake during the night and stay awake. Therefore, a routine would not be effective in resolving this issue; however, as we have seen, the parents' routine has helped Mary go down well and so part of their plan has worked and continues to work well.

Action point 2

I then challenged some of Jo and Andy's unhelpful thoughts – such as children should sleep all night – and told them how to work towards creating newer and more balanced thoughts – children go through periods of light sleep which is part of natural sleeping habits – using mindfulness techniques, which allow for change and flexibility.

Action point 3

I then advised Jo and Andy to adapt Mary's environment to create a space that has visual cues that can aid her understanding of what is expected of her at night and help to reassure her. I suggested placing pictures of Mary, her sister and mum and dad sleeping, appearing calm and contented where Mary could see them. Jo and Andy used a digital photo frame that they positioned near Mary's cot, so that when she wakes she is able to see images of her family to help her feel safe and reassured and provide her with cues that tell her it is time to sleep.

Action point 4

To manage night wakes, Jo and Andy need to take alternate nights to settle Mary. Movement and vibration can also be used to help calm Mary but not put her to sleep. The parents should use a graded form of responsiveness, which means that Mary is calm, then the parents do not need to intervene but can remain outside the room or beside her bed. However, they should only use the levels of responsiveness when Mary is unsettled and or crying.

The parents should also use different smells (a blend of essential oils that promote sleep), as cues at bedtime. They should each assign an individual smell and use this consistently so that Mary can associate the smell with each person who cares for her. Jo and Andy should use this smell for each time Mary wakes, as a cue to let her know what is expected of her.

I also advised Jo and Andy to use mindfulness and relaxation breathing techniques to help them sleep.

Action point 5

Jo and Andy need to remain consistent and monitor progress through thought and sleep records.

Outcome

Talking with the parents and working with their core beliefs was a challenging yet rewarding experience. The family could understand the theory behind the sleep plan, but found that their patterns of thinking were deeply engrained and that this often caused them high levels of frustration. However, they worked diligently on trying to challenge their previous thoughts and attitudes around their daughter's sleep and started to build more meaningful and manageable expectations. They realised that if Mary was happy and content in her room, then it was okay for them not to do anything. They accepted that sleep would come if they did not disturb the body rhythm too much, but helped Mary to focus more on sleep herself, rather than staying awake to see her parents in the night, as this kept her curious and engaged, and reinforced her body's rhythm pattern of nightly wakes.

Both parents completed thought diaries and tracked their automatic thoughts when Mary woke during the night. They then looked for the evidence that supported their thoughts, and used what we had discussed and their new information about sleep, to challenge their negative automatic thoughts and construct new, balanced and positive thoughts. Once they were able to change their thoughts, they felt less frustrated and angry when Mary would wake. This put them in the right state to respond or not respond to Mary as appropriate, and this in turn led to a more effective way of managing her sleep. This allowed Mary to use the various cues in the room to help her learn to put herself back off to sleep when she woke in the night.

In weeks 1 and 2, Jo and Andy worked on responding to Mary using action points 4 and 5 successfully.

By week 3 Mary's wakes remained the same, but what had changed was that she was only awake for 10–15 minutes and she was able to put herself back off to sleep without her parents' assistance.

At week 4 Jo and Andy reported that Mary was no longer waking in the night, or that they were not woken or disturbed by Mary's wakes in the night. Whichever scenario is true, the family were sleeping better and feeling better about their new situation.

CASE STUDY

Background

Stephanie was a young Englishwoman married to a Frenchman, Jack, who worked as a full-time teacher in the UK. Stephanie came to me with an initial concern regarding her son's sleeping habits. Christopher is a gorgeous, sociable and curious 18-month-old. Stephanie expressed a desire to help her son to sleep without controlled crying but wanted to acknowledge her husband's culture and their lifestyle. For Stephanie it was important that her husband had quality time with Christopher during the week, and as he often came home after 7pm she wanted a plan that would achieve both these goals. Jack also felt strongly that children should not be put on a strict routine and felt that family time and building relationships far outweighed the argument for a strict 7–7 bedtime arrangement. That said, Jack was fully aware of the requirement for good healthy sleeping and he too wished for his son to gain good quality healthy sleep. The family were currently co-sleeping using a cot that attached to the side of the parents' bed and this was how they were managing Christopher's frequent wakes. He would start off the night in his cot and then end up being in his mum and dad's bed for a cuddle usually after the second wake.

Christopher

Christopher was a happy, interested and loving baby, who enjoyed learning and exploring his safe world within his home. He was able to do this when his mother was present and enjoyed playing on his own and with his mother during the day. He would approach people cautiously during the day when his mum was present and often smile and make eye contact. He very rarely cried and when he did it was often due to being hurt or if his mother left the room. Christopher was totally in love with his mother and his eyes would follow her around the room and he would always look up periodically when he was playing to check if his Stephanie was still there and paying attention to him. Christopher would become distressed if his mother left the room or if she was not within eyesight. Christopher loved to play at his mother's feet and would prefer to play on her lap and cuddle and kiss her. When Christopher's father came home he would take a while to warm up. He had a good relationship with his father but always preferred his mother and when spending time with his father would enjoy this as long as his mother was present. Christopher would become distressed if his mother left the room and would attempt to follow her. Christopher would have dinner with his parents at 7.30 and his bedtime routine would start at 8.30.

Problem

Christopher would become distressed at bedtime if his mother left the room and he was alone with his dad. Christopher would also require his mother's presence until he fell asleep at night. He would need to be held until he feel asleep and then placed in his cot. Christopher would wake at least five times during the night and could only be settled by Mum. Dad felt left out and disconnected from his new family, he felt redundant at settling time and during the night. Mum felt exhausted from being the only one who was able to calm and care for Christopher at night. All the family were suffering from lack of sleep which was affecting their mood and ability to function well during the day.

The sleep problem was caused by separation anxiety due to the close bond Christopher had with his mother and the amount of time he spent with her. This was further maintained by the sleep cycle becoming set to wake during the night. Christopher was also dependent on his mother holding him in order to sleep and in the night he required this action again and again as he did not know how to get to sleep independently.

Separation anxiety is a natural phase for children Christopher's age to go through, but because his mother was his main caretaker, caring and playing with him during the day, there was very little opportunity for Christopher to get used to other people, or learn that he was safe when his mother was not present. Jack interacted with Christopher for a short time each evening after work but it was always with Stephanie and therefore he rarely had alone time with Christopher to build his relationship and be accepted by his son as an appropriate adult to calm and settle him at night. As Jack rarely got the opportunity to practise settling Christopher at night he failed to gain confidence in calming Chris, which maintained Jack's feelings of being redundant and disconnected from his family.

Dad's negative automatic thoughts were 'I cannot settle my son', 'I feel useless at night'.

Mum's negative automatic thoughts were 'My son can only be settled by me', 'Christopher will only sleep in my arms'.

Stephanie and Jack's fixed automatic thoughts also helped to keep their problem going as the more they had these thoughts the more they acted in a way that made them true. For example, Jack would often hang in the background rather than take the lead at bathtime. Stephanie would be on constant alert and if Christopher became distressed as she left the room she would rapidly return and comfort him. This reinforced Christopher's beliefs that only his mother could settle him.

The family wanted Christopher to be able to sleep in his own cot and move into his own room. He currently was sleeping in his parents' room and co-sleeping when he woke at night.

Christopher's problem sleep cycle

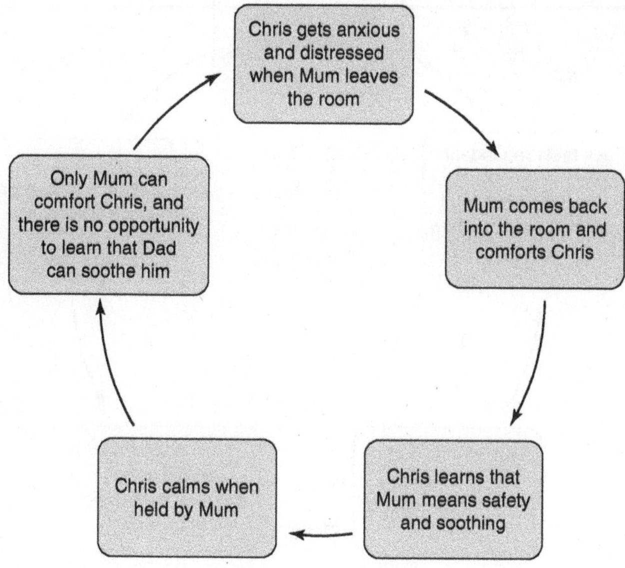

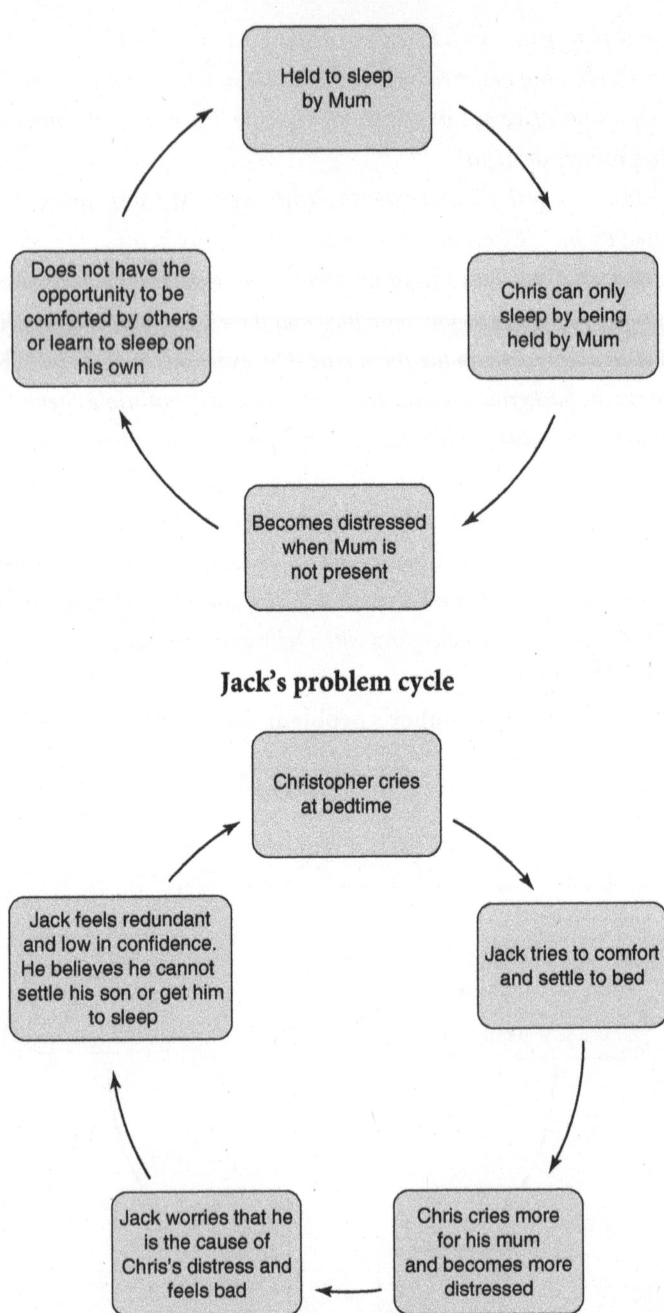

Jack's problem cycle

Stephanie's problem cycle

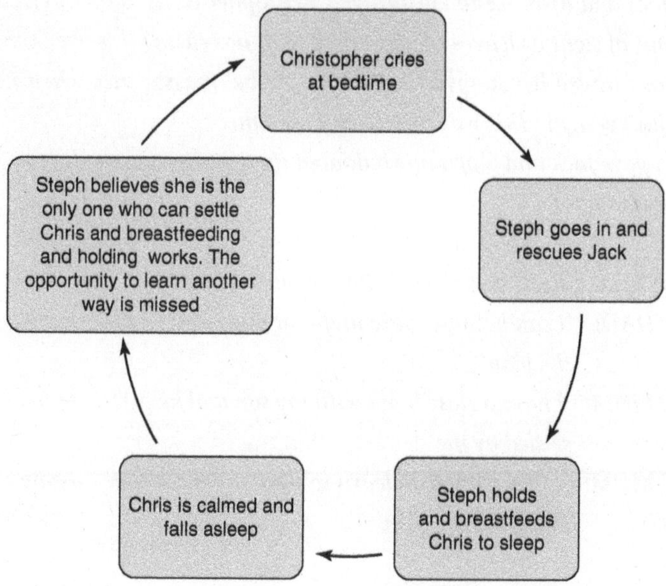

Plan

Stephanie and Jack were both authoritative in their style of parenting and I assessed Christopher as being an easy child. Therefore I devised a plan that looked at addressing the underlying problem of anxiety and dependency but also took account of Christopher and his family's wishes and parenting styles. This plan would give each parent the opportunity to challenge their thoughts about Christopher's sleeping habits and change how they respond to him during the day and, most importantly, at night. I would be requiring Stephanie to hang back and allow Jack to take more of a lead in settling Christopher.

Action point 1

First of all, I needed Chris to overcome his separation anxiety. I then challenged his parents' automatic thoughts. For four days before changing the bedtime routine, I asked Stephanie to use peek-a-boo games and distance to encourage Christopher to feel safe when she is out of sight or leaves to go to the toilet, increasing this over time. I encouraged her to give Christopher verbal reassurance when not in his eyesight. This was increased over time.

I gave Jack and Stephanie balanced thoughts to replace their negative ones:

> *DAD: 'I will be able to settle my son in time'*
> *DAD: 'I can become more useful at night-time by following the plan'*
> *MUM: 'I have a close bond with my son and he prefers to be settled by me'*
> *MUM: 'Christopher can learn to sleep in his cot over time by following the plan'*

Action point 2

I then wanted to start building Christopher's relationship bond with his dad. Jack used the school summer holidays engaged in active parenting with Christopher and taking the lead in most activities with Christopher during the day. When Stephanie left the room, Jack used this time to settle Christopher and Stephanie increased the time she left her two boys alone without returning if Christopher became unsettled, allowing Jack the opportunity to settle Christopher.

Action point 3

I then wanted Christopher to be able to fall asleep independently, and to achieve this I advised having a sleep routine at night-time that was based on a sequence of events rather than time: dinner, cuddles, bath, bottle, place in cot, stories, goodnight kisses. The bedtime plan started after dinner at around 8.30 and with Christopher in bed by around 9pm.

I suggested that Jack should start to put Christopher to bed for the first consecutive three nights of the plan in a row with Stephanie absent from the room. After that, his parents should take alternate nights to put Christopher to bed so only one parent at a time after three days of the start of the plan. Christopher would then be in bed awake for at least 10 minutes being read stories.

If Christopher became distressed, I advised his parents to use different levels of intervention to settle Christopher in a functional way both at settling time and at wakes throughout the night.

Once Christopher was asleep or calm, whichever was first, I said that the parent putting him to bed should leave the room.

Action point 4

In order for Christopher to stay in his cot throughout the night, I suggested the following plan:

Parents settle Christopher in cot.
They use different levels of intervention to match distress.
Parents to take alternate nights to settle.
There should be no rescuing of the other parent even if Christopher calls for the other parent.

Action point 5

In order for Christopher to move to his new room, I advised his parents to make it feel safe by using grounding tools such as pictures and sound. Christopher should also spend time in the day getting used to his new room.

Move Christopher into the room when his wakes are two or less per night, which should be around week 2.

Action point 6

To override the sleep cycle, Christopher's parents should practise consistency, and match the distress to the appropriate levels of intervention.

Use PAUSE to allow Christopher to resettle by himself.

Stephanie and Jack should do this for the remaining four weeks of a six-week plan.

Action point 7

I asked Stephanie and Jack to use a sleep chart to monitor their progress.

Outcome

By challenging the negative thoughts they had and applying the tools to overcome separation anxiety, both Stephanie and Jack found that this paved the way for changing their behaviour at night. Christopher coped well with the changes and as Jack had spent more time with Christopher he felt more able to take over the settling process at night. Christopher had the opportunity to get used to feeling safe when he did not see his mum. This meant that when Jack took over at night Christopher was not as distressed and he could focus on going to sleep. As Dad had challenged his negative automatic thoughts and replaced them with more helpful thoughts he could focus on applying the techniques to help calm Christopher in a confident fashion.

When Stephanie and Jack started the plan, Stephanie found it hard to distance herself; she acknowledged that she needed to be with Christopher during the day as much as he needed to be with her. She had to work hard at challenging her negative automatic thoughts. When she did she noticed her own anxiety reduce and she was able to see the evidence that by allowing Jack to be more involved Christopher was less clingy and seemed to enjoy the time with his dad. She felt more relaxed and found her daytime interaction with Christopher was much improved.

Jack found settling Christopher challenging for the first day, and he had to hold him a lot for the first night, which Christopher accepted. Christopher fell asleep in Jack's arms and he then transferred him to the cot. Christopher woke three times that night. Jack used the different levels of interventions to calm Christopher from within the cot and did not pick him up to sleep with him and his mother. The second night Jack was able to settle Christopher and read him a story with little distress. That night Christopher woke twice. Towards the end of the first week of the plan, Stephanie found it very easy to settle Christopher who eagerly went into his bed and listened to his stories. Stephanie stayed with him until he fell asleep, which took 30 minutes. By week 2 Christopher was moved to his own room and the parents took well to settling alternate nights. By the third week Christopher was sleeping all night with the odd wake in the night.

By week 6 Christopher was sleeping until 7.30am and waking only once a week. He was able to settle himself or be settled by either parent within 10 minutes.

The fact that your child has his own temperament echoes my earlier statement that it is not your fault that your child is having problems establishing a healthy sleeping pattern. You can see here that the cautious baby will probably be feeling lonely or anxious and that this is a barrier to sleep. Knowing this means your solution to helping them sleep is a simple one: help them to feel safer and secure at night and get them independently used to their surroundings. Our little wilful baby finds it hard to settle and so will need to settle in and get used to his environment. This will take time and patience.

Now that you have matched your parenting style to your child's temperament we can look at what behaviours you will use for each issue that gets in the way of sleep.

Chireal's Tip Bits

Become your own sleep consultant: learn what works for you and your family.

Chapter 7

Charm your baby to sleep

Did you know: Sleeping well speeds up your metabolism and lack of sleep is linked to obesity?

IT'S OFTEN SO HARD TO MUSTER UP THE ENERGY TO SMILE AND be jolly when you are tired. We know that one of the side effects of lack of sleep is irritability and low mood so it's natural that summoning up the high motivation and positive attitude necessary when teaching your baby to self-soothe may be a significant challenge. However, I am going to ask you to tap into your love language and love bomb your child; these feelings are always there even if they are just lurking under the surface and they don't require a huge amount of energy to summon. In fact, I am not requiring you to use a massive amount of energy, I just need you to use your charm, your eyes, your smile and your voice to coax your child and win them over to get them working alongside you through love. Make eye contact with your child and maintain it, smile often and frequently with your child no matter what, use your positive emotions and encouraging body language to charm your child. Through the soft sound of your voice and the gentle tones you are using she will engage, calm and comply because she wants to see you smile, she wants to feel that love and the more you give it to her the more she will try harder to get it. Your small baby is so enamoured by your face already and before she is even born she knows your voice – this is your secret weapon so use it for sleep. Use your voice in a way that will grab your child's attention. Babies love singing, and if you have a voice that can carry a beautiful note, I would use this first and foremost. Babies are moved emotionally by the sound of song and your singing voice can encourage the most powerful reactions of love – this type of love-bombing through sound will have your baby falling in love with you every time. If you are like me and your singing voice won't have you audition for *The X Factor* anytime soon, don't fret as you too can use your voice for love and charming your baby to sleep. Use long, low tones as you talk to your child in a rhythmical fashion. Have a statement that you use often that is reassuring. My favourite is: 'Mummy's here, you are safe, it's just sleep.' Saying this over and over again will guarantee that your baby is charmed into feeling immense love for you and will charm them to slumber. I advise my parents to always use statements rather than questions; this is because questions invite a response and your baby is then primed to attend and be alert. This is not helpful to your goal of getting your baby in a dreamy state for sleep. So use statements rather than questions and repeat the statements. Keep your tone the same and your baby will feel reassured rather than anxious. They will comply because it feels right, because they feel right; they feel right because they feel love; when babies are feeling loved they are relaxed and when they are relaxed they sleep. And when our babies are relaxed, calm and asleep we become relaxed, calm and happy.

The gentle sleep system is a way of communicating, bonding and reassuring your child so that he is able to gain a natural sleeping pattern through nurturing. This method is achieved through using CBT, mindfulness and attachment tools. The way we think about how our babies sleep, and our problems, is the cognitive sleep cycle. The next thing we need to do is to figure out and identify the barriers to sleep and work out how we will break the cycle. The mindfulness technique is where we acknowledge how important our emotions are and work towards managing them so that we are in the right mood and state to change our babies' behaviour. The attachment tools are the element of behavioural change, the bit where I coach you on how to respond in a functional way, what to do to calm your baby, where to respond, how to lovingly communicate with your baby and send the right message based on your parenting style and her temperament, through the use of essential tools, non-verbal and verbal communication, adapting the environment, different levels of responsiveness, PAUSE and consistency.

Non-verbal communication makes up 70 per cent of communication and therefore our babies are take the lead from the positions of our bodies, our facial expressions, sound and movement. Research has shown that newborn babies an hour old are able to respond to and mimic our facial expressions. This is an amazing insight because it means that we can let our babies know what is expected of them by simply changing our facial expressions; we can shape and change their behaviour by simply opening and closing our eyes or mouths.

Try this out by charming your baby to sleep. Maintain eye contact and give them a gentle half-smile. Hold their gaze and breathe evenly. When your baby responds positively, calms down and relaxes, give them a big smile as a reward – this will encourage them to repeat this behaviour because you have told them it's good. This is a simple yet very powerful way of encouraging the behaviour you crave. You have charmed your baby just by using your eyes.

Some advice suggests that you shouldn't make eye contact with your child when you are sleep training. I am unclear as to the reasoning behind this suggestion. However, I can assure you that when your baby is distressed and needs you but won't let you hold them, eye contact is an excellent way to soothe your child and communicate love when your child can't or won't 'hear' you. This use of love language or love-bombing your child to sleep is an effective and sure-fire way of building and maintaining that bond you need to help your child acquire a healthy attachment. We know that your heartbeat can reduce the levels of cortisol (the stress hormone) that your baby produces when she cries.

You can see how this compassionate cycle of loving your baby to sleep works and how amazingly effective it is. And this is all coming from you – how you communicate with your child, how you use your love language to soothe your child and help to make them feel safe in your presence. This is the ultimate way we enable our children to self-soothe, by first loving them, communicating love and then charming them into a feeling of safety, showing them that sleep is a good place and state to be in and that anxiety or worry have no place here. With this approach and method of charming your baby to sleep you are sending the message that your baby is safe whether you are in the room or outside.

Be consistent at bedtime

Consistency is often confused with having a rigid routine. In my view, consistency is more about the message you give your baby and allows you more flexibility. I want you to focus on sending your child the same message each and every bedtime. You are allowed to behave differently, you can be in a different environment such as your own parents' home and start your routine at a different time; for example, in the summer you may choose to go out and come home slightly later. This is all fine and, to me, doesn't show a lack of consistency.

Consistency is about sending the same message over and over again. Your message to your baby at bedtime is that she is safe: she is safe with you and she is safe without you. This is the message we want our children to hear and feel. So you will have your sequence of events – your cues that signal bedtime – and you will follow that sequence, but you can be flexible in your approach depending on how your child feels. Some days your child may need more or less attention based on their mood, and the same goes for you too.

To help you with knowing what you can do to support a consistent bedtime I have set out some points for you to consider incorporating into your plan.

Bedtime actions

* Find out what your baby likes and do it, and then repeat it
* Make bedtime calm but fun
* Spend more time in your child's room in the day so that it's not just a place you send them to be alone and sleep alone
* Make their room a place of wonder, calmness and safety. Use calming colours and visual aids such as pictures of you
* Use blue and red night-lights to help promote sleep and maintain a natural sleep cycle
* Create curiosity around bedtime; make it mysterious and fun through story and your imagination
* Slow things down, pace yourself
* Use essential oils to induce sleep. Burn or place in infusers essential oils that promote sleep such as jasmine, sandalwood and lavender
* Use classical music

Chireal's Tip Bits

The golden key to your confidence is opening your eyes to your everyday successes, of which there are many.

Improve night-time sleep during the day

When we charm our babies to feel good at bedtime and enjoy the process of going to sleep we are creating the perfect environment for good sleep at night. We are encouraging good daytime sleep also because the better your child's night-time sleep the better daytime sleep will be. Naps will organically adapt to the pattern your child is developing, so if your child is self-setting at night-time, she will be able to settle at daytime naps, and nap length will automatically increase because your child is able to self-settle and move on to the next phase of the sleep cycle independently. Your job in both these scenarios is to provide the right environment and be charming, consistent and confident. Your role is to get your child into the right state for sleep and limit their distress; your child's job is to learn to fall to sleep independently.

You and your baby have your very own unique dance that you do every day, and every member of your family will dance with your baby in a different way. The dance you do with your baby during the day is your interaction, your communication, and your behaviour. It's how you get to know one another; it's your very own special unique relationship that no one knows except you and your baby. This bond that you are building with your baby is special because, as I have mentioned before, your baby learns how to respond to you and you learn how to respond to them. This is how she is built – we call this in the psychology field classical conditioning. Our children learn what to expect and when to expect it, and this stays true for both night and day. We can improve our children's sleep habits at night-time by making sure that we do the same dance at night-time as we do in the day. Put simply, we need to be consistent in the message that we are sending our babies in the day, and that has to be the same message that we are sending at bedtime and during the night.

Some of my parents have told me that in the day when their baby has called out for them they have not used the PAUSE method and have responded to their child using one of the top-level interventions, which is usually picking up their child. That's all well and good you may think as it stops baby from crying and she is now calm and all is well with the world. Well, let's take a look at the message we are sending our babies with this response. If you pick up your child each and every time your baby cries then over time your baby learns that being picked up is the only way to be soothed. This is okay if we are able to pick our baby up each and every time she cries. However, usually this is not the case and we are not always present when our baby cries. We also want to begin to teach our babies to self-soothe so we need to show them other ways they can be soothed, for example, with our presence, voice, touch, movement, etc.

Where this becomes important is at night-time. Our babies' expectations of our behaviour do not change; they are very good at being consistent. In fact, they are very good at shaping our behaviour, they are the experts. But we need to become the experts of them and pretty quickly if we are to change and improve how they sleep at night and for naps. Now, your little baby is expecting that when you put her to bed at night, you will respond to her in the same way you did during the day, when you immediately, without the PAUSE, met her need with a top-level intervention response. This is what she wants and this is what she knows works. The problem is that your expectations have changed – at night-time you don't want to respond to your child in the same way you do during the day. Not because you don't love her or that you don't want to help her – you just want to sleep.

As parents our expectations at night change and we want our babies to be soothed and settled by our voice alone or by herself in her cot. We automatically think that just because it's night-time our babies should somehow know that the rules have changed. Our babies' expectations stay the same – they have no idea it's night-time or that you require sleep, and they just need you to do the same loving dance you have always done, because they love it and because it works. So what's the problem, they think? A big problem for you as it means that you are awake and so are they – it's night-time and you don't want to 'dance', you want to sleep.

Chireal's Tip Bits

Unless your baby has soiled her nappy or has a medical need you don't need to change her nappy in the night ... let her sleep.

I tell my parents that if they want their babies to sleep at night they must send the same message during the day as they do at night, do the same dance, as it were. It's only right and fair that we give our babies the opportunity to learn and do something different at night and learn the new dance. By doing this we are teaching our babies with the PAUSE method that his needs will always be met and that they can learn to self-soothe. We can do this by matching our response to the level of their distress during the day. In the day, teach your baby to self-soothe by using lower levels of intervention and grade up as required based on their distress. By dancing with your baby in this way, he learns that he can be soothed in different ways. He learns that he too can PAUSE and at night-time he won't expect to be immediately picked up, fed or rocked. He learns in the PAUSE that he can self-soothe. He is calmed by the fact that he knows what to expect, you have shaped his environment so that he feels safe, comforted and not alone. He knows and trusts that you will always meet his needs and so he can focus on the business of going back to sleep, by moving seamlessly and independently on to the next phase of the sleep cycle.

By changing what you do in the day you can change your baby's sleep habits at night. Even if you danced in a different way and you want to change your baby's expectations at night-time to improve your sleep, I would urge you strongly to change the dance in the day before you embark on changing anything you do with your baby at night. This is important for two reasons: firstly, you are giving your baby an opportunity to learn how you will now be responding to them, and secondly by teaching them and laying the foundations of your new dance in the day you will minimise and reduce the tears, distress and tantrums you might expect from your baby if you suddenly spring a new way of responding to them in the night-time, when we are all at our least tolerant.

Key points

- The message you are sending your baby is: you will always meet his needs
- Before you change night-time behaviour spend three to four days teaching your baby to respond to different levels of intervention/responsiveness in the day

- Use the daytime to shape and change the way you dance with each other
- Give your baby a chance to learn and accept the new ways you are dancing with them
- Change daytime behaviour (dance) first
- Send the same message at night-time
- Respond to your child both in the day and night with PAUSE and different levels of responsiveness
- Every family member should send the same message even though they may act in a different way
- Avoid the sleep traps at night such as when feeding, rocking to sleep, rescuing the other parent

Chireal's Tip Bits

Base your routine on the time your baby wakes up for the day. Your more flexible and effective guide to feeding and sleeping starts here.

Levels of responsiveness

Theories on how to respond effectively to your child's distress fall into two main camps: the argument that children should be left (extinction) and the argument that children should be with you at all times (baby-wearing). These are two very controversial positions. In my experience parents naturally want to take care of their little ones and are searching for an effective way to tend to their child's needs in a way that fits in with their family's lifestyle. So there is a desperate need for some common sense middle ground talk here. This comes in the shape of responsiveness.

> *Chireal's Tip Bits*
>
> It's not a question of whether you attend to your child's cries, it's a matter of *how.*

At different times in your child's development she will need different types of care and therefore your actions and behaviours have to be in line with meeting your child's needs through all the stages of their development. By responding to your child and teaching them you are there for them you enable them to develop self-soothing techniques. By being consistent and sending the same message to your baby she will soon learn to tolerate being away from you and develop a sense of self while still being a beautiful social creature.

The other golden key that will help you unlock the door to sleep success is matching your intervention to your child's level of distress. We can grade the different types of responding to our babies, from the least intensive to the most:

Levels of responsiveness

Response and reassurance (Parent)	Levels of distress (Child)
6) Pick up (move)	Constant distress crying
5) Cuddle (from within the cot), deep breathing and cheek-to-cheek	Escalating crying in waves
4) Touch (pat rock, bum rock)	Crying
3) Proximity (getting closer)	Cough-style crying
2) Verbal reassurance	Frustration/crying
1) Your presence	Moaning/frustration

When your child whimpers there is no need for you to go in with your top-level intervention as you will have nowhere to go, except out of the door, if your child continues to be in distress. You should save your most powerful intervention – picking your child up – until you really need it, i.e. when your child is crying. Matching your response to your child's level of distress gives your child the space to know how she should respond.

The table above can be used for all children no matter how old. Your aim as a parent is to apply the attachment tools functionally. So pick up your baby only when she is distressed. When your baby wakes in the night the responses above will calm your baby. The length of time it takes for your baby to be calmed by your actions will depend on three things: your baby's temperament, your state (if you are not in a calm state it will take longer) and how severe your sleep issue is. You will know this by your score on the quiz you took on pages 68–69. This should inform you how your baby may react. The crucial point is that your baby will be calmed by the above actions.

Presence is often underrated as a tool to calm our children but I want us to go back to the fundamental basis of what we know about our babies: seeing you is a reward and a powerful one at that, so on your plan I want you to walk into your baby's room with confidence, fully aware of how calming and positive your presence is. Before you go on to use any other types of reassurance responses, use your presence. Use your presence when your baby is frustrated and moaning just before she starts to become upset.

Verbal reassurance should be your next grade up on the levels of responsiveness, using calm statements, reassuring your baby with words, song or sounds. Spend some time allowing your baby to hear and respond to you before you move up a level to the next behavioural tool or down to just your presence when she is calm. You can verbally reassure your baby when she is frustrated and while she is crying. If her cries escalate then you grade up, if she is calm then you grade down. Allow your baby to learn that she can be calmed by your presence and your voice. By using verbal reassurance and your presence you are extremely powerful and effective. And your baby will respond pretty quickly and be soothed by just these two elements.

Some babies will find it harder to be settled by presences and verbal reassurance alone in the first few days of your plan and if your baby is like this, don't worry: the main point is that you are meeting your child's needs, you are present and you are building trust and bonding with your child, even when she is upset. You are with her and the next steps will be extremely effective in calming down a distressed infant.

Touch and cuddling is such a strong antidote for stress and crying in babies, couple that touch with you being close to your baby and you have a very potent combination. Use this when your baby's cries begin to escalate; this is often signalled by a coughing cry. Touch your baby, use cheek-to-cheek contact, cupping their face, deep breathing in their ear and rocking them from side to side. Try not to pick up your baby but reassure her while she is still in the cot. Rather than bringing your baby to you, go to your baby, meet her where she is at. This has a few benefits: your baby is soothed in her sleeping environment, she can build a positive association with the cot and it's easier and more consistent for establishing a natural sleeping habit for your baby to remain where she is going to be sleeping all night, than transferring her back into the cot once she is calm. The vast majority of unsettled babies will be calmed by using touch, movement and cuddles in this way.

For those particularly spirited babies, the babies that find it hard to tolerate change, you may need to use your top-level intervention quite frequently during the first week of your plan, allowing your baby to first get used to you using this in a functional way. Once you are able to calm her and you have created some space, you can then introduce some of the tools lower down the intervention table and get her used to those in a gradual way.

Before you start on changing how you respond to your child's sleeping habit or problem you have to look at how you parent and communicate with them in the day. I suggest that you will be more successful in shaping your baby's nap during the day and sleep at night when you first change how you respond to them in a general day-to-day interaction.

When changing how you respond to your child it is important to start with practice during the day as it is only fair that you give her a chance to recognise that you are changing how you respond to her before night-time when she is at her least tolerant. By laying the foundations in the day, you will show your child just how easily she can be calmed by just your voice and/or your presence as opposed to always needing to be picked up or fed. You will then have the opportunity to move up and down the level of responsiveness depending on your child's level of distress. By moving up should the need arise you are being an effective and responsive parent to your baby and thereby reducing their overall distress and increasingly the likelihood of them sleeping well. You will be more effective in calming your baby and managing your emotions. By introducing this new way of behaving with your child in the day you are paving the way for your child to be calm and soothed easily without distress at night-time. When you see that you can soothe your child in a different way this will undoubtedly make you more motivated and excited about making those changes at night. An example of this would be if your baby were used to being held every time she cries. Your job in the day is to get your baby used to and accepting being calmed by your presence, eye contact, your voice and by your touch, as opposed to being picked up straight away. Your baby learns that she can be calmed by these other methods.

This will ensure that she is less likely to cry or become distressed when you change how you respond to her at settling time, naps and wakes during the night.

Once your baby is responding to your interventions you can begin to address nap and daytime sleep. If your infant struggles during this learning phase of changing her sleeping behaviour, for example, you might miss a nap or the nap is a shortened one, all is not lost. Your baby is continually learning and so are you. At each opportunity for a nap or when she is upset you will use the levels of responsiveness and each time you do it is an opportunity for your baby to learn a new way to be settled. Put your baby down for a nap when she is next due for one in order to stay on track, and in between ensure that your activities and interactions are not too overstimulating and give yourself a break too. I do not want your whole day to be consumed by sleep and the process of getting your baby to be calm to learn to sleep.

If for the first day or two the late afternoon naps do not go according to plan moving bedtime by 30 minutes to an hour earlier will ensure that you avoid your baby being overtired.

How to calm your child when you are not there

We have just discussed how to soothe your child and teach her to self-soothe in your presence. The next step is to help your child to self-soothe when you are not there. Night-time is the longest time our children are away from us, so it's only natural that she should be a little anxious. The younger she is the more anxious and confused she may be. It is not possible, no matter how attentive you are as a parent, for you to be with your child every minute of their life. So we need to find a way to enable our children to feel safe when they are alone. This is important for a number of reasons: it boosts their ability to self-soothe, it teaches them that they are safe and it allows you to get on with the many other jobs you have to do without the worry that your baby needs you the moment they open their eyes. Also, if we go back to what we know about sleep, you will remember that our babies spend more time in light sleep throughout their whole sleep cycle so, essentially, our light-sleeping babies will be on some level conscious of their surroundings. An anxious baby will wake fully and seek reassurance on each and every light sleep phase of the sleep cycle. That's a lot of wakes in one 45-minute cycle actually. I don't need to tell you that this is not ideal! The trick here is to teach our little ones how to pass through to the next phase of their sleep cycle independently, without the need or urge to call out for us. So you need to do something different – you leave pieces of you behind.

The minute your baby is born, she is able to communicate, mirror your behaviour and recognise your voice, smell and face. Use this to your advantage and, at every opportunity both day and night, use your baby's strong senses to let her feel safe and comforted. If you wear perfume, spray it in your child's room so the rooms smells of you. Sing to your baby and sing often; smile, laugh and make eye contact with your child to help develop her social cues and awareness.

You represent warmth, love and safety to your child, and you want her to feel safe, warm and loved. To do this you need to create an environment in which your child sleeps where she feels safe, warm and loved. Shape your world and theirs so that your essence shines through: this will be the music you like to play, the pictures you have on the walls, the style of lighting, the colours and decor of your home. Even down to how you position your furniture will give your space a feeling of safety and warmth.

Key points here for you to consider:

* Pictures of you and your family in your child's room are excellent grounding tools to help your child feel reassurance when you are not present and affords you some time to get to him before his cries escalate.
* Wear their bed sheet down your top and place it on their bed. This is a good example of leaving pieces of you behind to help your child feel safe and secure. Your smell will help to limit your baby's distress and make them feel secure and safe.
* Record your voice reading or singing and play it at bed- and naptimes. Like the bedsheet, this is an example of a grounding tool that will help your child feel safe when you are not with them and give you time to get to them before you use the levels of responsiveness.
* Keep their space warm before placing them down. This is an excellent tool that helps your baby accept her bed environment as you have limited the difference between the warmth of you and the temperature of the cot. By limiting the difference you are reducing the likelihood of your child becoming distressed and/or rejecting being put down.

The behavioural part of the CBT model deals with how you change your communication with your child. This includes all the non-verbal and verbal elements we discussed when using the different levels of responsiveness and matching this to your baby's distress. I have shown you how you can respond and communicate in a way that breaks your vicious cycle and puts you well along your path of change now your plan is in its implementation phase. These will form part of your helpful behaviours and will replace the unhelpful behaviours you did in the past that kept you locked in your vicious cycle. These are all attachment-based tools which are designed to promote bonding, trust and reassurance for your baby, as well as changing their behavioural response as you are communicating change (which forms a large part of the CBT model) in a way that will reduce your baby's distress and yours. The different levels of reassurance are the cornerstone of the gentle sleep system.

The functional application of the tools will lay the foundation for a good sleep pattern. Work on changing your response to your baby during the day before you change anything at bedtime. Laying the foundation (in other words, practising in the day) is at the heart of helping to shape your baby's sleep pattern with limited distress. Taking change slowly at a pace you and your baby can manage and using this in a sequenced and mindful way is the gentle sleep system.

Other behavioural changes will be less subtle, but equally as powerful and important, and are based around how you may use or adapt/change the environment so that you are helping your child break their vicious cycle by shaping and changing the message you are sending them. Previously unhelpful actions would reinforce undesired beliefs for you and your baby and keep your problem going. By changing the message you send your child you will be helping your baby and you establish a natural sleep pattern through nurturing. The next chapter will discuss attachment tools further.

Chapter 8

Attachment tools to aid sleep

Did you know: Research states that having parents nearby at night may help babies regulate their stress response during the day?

What is attachment theory?

Hopefully, we have all known love and what it feels like to be loved. That love we feel is what we call the 'relational bond' and this bond is our attachment to other human beings. Many people are not aware that attachment theory and attachment parenting are two very different things. It's important to point this out early on as attachment parenting is viewed by some as being quite controversial and most people who are well versed on the subject will have pretty strong views one way or another.

Attachment parenting was developed from the principles of attachment theory into a parenting concept by Dr William Sears and his wife Martha. They talk about a set of behaviours, such as baby-wearing and co-sleeping, that will help your baby sleep, grow and socialise. Not all parents are comfortable with some of the suggestions made by Dr Sears and other parents who may like the idea find it very difficult to achieve as the principles can seem demanding and time-consuming and leave little room for anything other than baby care. This principle is baby-centric and this is good for the families that it works for. However, we want to find a middle ground that takes into account today's busy world, a path that maintains the love connection and love bond that is doable for all families of all compositions. Not all mothers can breastfeed, not all parents can stay at home with their baby and not all families can co-sleep.

The origin of attachment theory can be traced back to 1958 and John Bowlby's 'The Nature of the Child's Tie to his Mother' and Harry Harlow's *The Nature of Love.* John Bowlby was a pioneer in the study of psychology and he introduced the concept of 'attachment'. He researched heavily the mother–child bond that is formed in the early days of a child's life. This important bond was seen as a golden key that allowed babies to understand how to behave and love. The research has moved on somewhat since those early days and what we now know is that the first love attachment a baby has is typically the mother, but that babies can form bonds with another caregiver and, more importantly, they can form this bond with more than one person. This allows our babies to love all members of their family equally, which means that all members of the family can be involved in the baby's care, shaping their behaviour in a positive way.

Attachment theory has led to a new understanding of child development. Children develop different styles of attachment based on experiences and interactions with their caregivers, and this can be positive or negative. Having a child with a secure attachment is what we all strive for when we parent and raise our families. Attachment theory has become the dominant theory used today in the study of infant and toddler behaviour, and in the fields of infant mental health, the treatment of children and related fields. Interestingly, many evidence-based treatment approaches are based on attachment theory when it comes to the issue of sleep. This theory until today has been strangely absent. This is why I emphasise bonding tools (the love connection) as they limit your baby's stress and distress and helps them to trust us and feel safe and secure at all times.

Briefly, four different attachment styles have been identified in children:

Attachment style	Parental style	Resulting adult characteristics
Secure	Aligned with the child; in tune with the child's emotions	Able to create meaningful relationships; empathetic; able to set appropriate boundaries
Avoidant	Unavailable or rejecting	Avoids closeness or emotional connection; distant; critical; rigid; intolerant
Ambivalent	Inconsistent and sometimes intrusive parent communication	Anxious and insecure; controlling; blaming; erratic; unpredictable; sometimes charming
Disorganised	Ignored or didn't see child's needs; parental behaviour was frightening/traumatising	Chaotic; insensitive; explosive; abusive; untrusting even while craving security

Individuals who experience confusing, frightening or broken emotional communications during their infancy often grow into adults who have difficulty understanding their own emotions and the feelings of others.

The gentle sleep system works on the premise that all families have the capacity to love, bond and create a healthy attachment with their child and this book will show you how to implement these techniques in your own family. The methods used in the gentle sleep system rely heavily on the theory of attachment: my methods are about promoting the attachment bond between parent and child and building love and trust between parent and child. The reason for this is because our children need to be loved, they need comfort, they need us to soothe them and they need us to teach them how to navigate their own worlds. The mother–child attachment bond shapes infants' brains, profoundly influencing their self-esteem, expectations of others and their ability to attract and maintain successful relationships. The success, or failure, of our first love – the attachment bond – has a life-long effect.

The gentle sleep system acknowledges how important this bond is as, without this attachment and care, our children will grow up unable to socialise or form and maintain healthy relationships. Our children need to feel safe with us around and safe without us around. In order for this to happen we must and should always respond to their needs and use tools that promote the attachment bond, the love connection. Children who feel safe sleep, and children who are able to function independently sleep! Children who are given boundaries sleep!

Tips and tricks for calming your newborn baby

- Toe to base: place your baby in his bed space so that his feet touch the base. This makes him feel secure and safe and ensures that you do not activate the startle reflex that could make him more awake or cause him to become distressed.
- To calm your baby in his cot, touch the top of his head with a slight pressure, put light pressure on his chest, or cup his face and cheek on one side when his head is moving from side to side and let him snuggle into the palm of your hand.
- Keep your baby's cot on an incline around 30-degree angle with head end higher. This helps prevent acid reflux.
- Swaddle your baby with his arms out after four months.

- Ensure your swaddle is secure but not tight to avoid overheating.
- Use essential oils in your baby's room as a smell cue.
- Use wheat-bag warmers to heat your baby's sleep space before you put him down. Remove once he is lying down.
- When your baby is ill, keep him in his room to maintain a positive association with the room. Meet his needs, hold him even if he falls asleep on you – this is okay. Be functional in your behaviour, use the PAUSE method and when he is well get back on track.

As your child gets used to being calmed by varying degrees of responsiveness then the urge to take them out of the cot will reduce. The aim here is to get your child to be soothed by your voice and presence and this will pave the way for your exit strategy. You are trying to get your child less dependent on your actions and presence and more independent on their ability to self-soothe. By following my method of introducing your baby to the levels of responsiveness in the day, working over a period of a week in settling techniques your baby will respond positively to your touch, voice or presence and be calmed. Once your baby is in her cot and calmed or asleep, whichever is first, you will be able to leave the room. Some babies (those with a cautious temperament) will need you to stay in the room for longer periods until they are asleep. This is okay, you will just have to gradually retreat. Gradual retreat is a planned and staged exit strategy that prepares your baby for leaving. This stage will involve you being close to your baby for the first couple of days and then being in the middle of the room with the door open for a few nights and then being outside the room and waiting ready to respond to your child with the reassurance levels should they become anxious again.

Attachment tools to teach your baby to sleep well

> *Chireal's Tip Bits*
>
> You don't have to ignore your child in order to help them sleep.

Attachment bonds are as unique as we are. We can be flexible and shape our babies' lives in many different ways. Parents don't have to be perfect – that is an unrealistic expectation and goal to have. It's okay to be different, it's okay to be 'good enough' – you will not do any long-lasting damage if you are not 100 per cent perfect all of the time. You do not have to always be in tune with your baby's emotions, but when you are working on sleep with your child it does help to be emotionally available the majority of the time. The first two years of your child's life is when he will do the most growing. Being able to form a foundation of a secure attachment bond will mean that your child will become self-confident, trusting, hopeful and comfortable in the face of conflict. As an adult, he will be flexible, creative, hopeful and optimistic. So let's start as we mean to go on because sleep is just another type of behaviour and we need to manage sleep in the same thoughtful and considerate way that we do our children's daytime behaviour. These attachment tools will help you as they will form part of your tool box of things to use as and when you need them. They are very successful in calming babies and helping them sleep. These tools can be things that you start to change prior to implementing your plan or use as trouble shooting when you are already on your plan and things may not be going as anticipated.

Adapt the sleeping environment

Your space and your child's space is one of the most overlooked sources of sleeping aids and supports. We often decorate our children's rooms or nursery as spaces that are fun and full of activity, designed with the major brands or the latest Disney obsession. However, your child's space should instead be used to enhance the quality of his sleep by creating an inviting, cosy yet calm environment. We can do this simply by choosing calming pastel colours, ensuring that we don't overcrowd the room, and place mirrors so they are not opposite the baby's bed (a baby seeing another baby moving in the mirror may cause anxiety). Strategically place furniture so that your child feels safe, take down any items that may be hanging on wardrobes as these may cause anxiety at night-time as your child may not be able to make out the shapes and become distressed, and finally use pictures of the family on the wall rather than animals or TV characters as these may cause anxiety, nightmares and even contribute to night terrors.

Mask external sound

To minimise the risk of your child being woken by external sound, whether that's from within the home or outside, use a sound conditioner or white noise machine. These machines are specifically designed to enhance sleep and mask noise. This can be especially helpful if you have more than one child and can really help with behavioural management issues and keep you mindful and focused on your sleep plan as you will not need to worry about your other child being woken up during he implantation phase of your plan should your baby start to become unsettled.

Same place to sleep, same place to wake

You know what it feels like to be disorientated when you wake from a sleep, or if you've fallen asleep on the sofa and have to make the journey to your bed, or waking up with a jolt when you have nodded off on a bus or train and think you have missed your stop. When we wake from a sleep state we are confused and disorientated and it takes a little while for us to get our bearings. Well, imagine how our babies feel when they wake somewhere they did not fall asleep, like falling asleep in a parent's arms or while feeding. Think about how distressing this may be for them if they wake to find themselves in a new environment. To reduce anxiety and confusion and respect your child's sleeping pattern I advise that where he wakes is where you should put him down to sleep. For your child to learn to sleep well, being consistent with his sleeping environment will go a long way to helping him sleep through the night. Keeping on being consistent, and the use of grounding tools – such as smells and sounds – will ensure your baby feels safe and calm, and this is the perfect state to establish natural sleeping patterns.

Prepare your child for sleeping (sequence of events)

Going to bed should be a seamless transition from a wakeful state to sleep and you can aid this process for your child by sign-posting bedtime. By signposting, your child can see, feel and hear all the triggers that let her know it's time for bed. Our little babies are amazing as this associated learning is innate. We can tap into this effective learning style simply by showing them, through sight, sound and our behaviour, what they should be doing and when. Do not underestimate what your baby is capable of. Cues and sequences of events can be made up of major and minor cues and you can place them in order of what suits your family and you can have as many as you like. It is the order that you do them in that is key to your baby knowing what is happening in their world and the consistency of your delivery. This style of routine allows you to alter times and environment and still have your baby sleep, well, like a baby.

Here is an example of cues and sequences:

Dinner – tidy – dim lights – put classical music on – prepare milk and 'bedtime box' (this is a bag in which you put all the items you will need to complete the bedtime routine: you may place bottle, dummy, comforters, story books in there – bath – feed – get dressed – place in cot – read story – kiss goodnight.

Rolling with resistance – know when to touch and when to let go

This is a term that I find so useful when coaching my parents as quite often they don't know how to respond to their baby when he is arching their back and appears to want to jump out of his parent's arms. When babies are so upset that they seem to not respond to what we say or do, most of my parents report that they hold on tighter, they cuddle their child even closer when they behave in this way. Another example where parents struggle is when their child begins to stand up in the cot and refuses to lie down, and my parents tell me they get into the game of lying them down only for them to jump up again. This can go on for some time as the baby loves this new game and the parents are at their wit's end thinking that their child will never assume the correct position that indicates to them that they will comply with our parental wishes and drift off to sleep.

Both these situations are challenging and tough for both parent and child. In some cases it can easily turn into a battle and create a more wakeful state, which prolongs the whole process of falling asleep. It's important to trust in the power of your presence and know that you don't have to hold your child to show love, This is where eye contact, song, breath and your voice come into play as you can use these to help calm your baby.

Roll along with his resistance. Put him down safely either on a flat surface or in his cot if he is arching away from you, and wait for him to reach out for you again before you pick him up. Don't fight with him, accept his distress and discomfort and give him some space. Cuddle him when he shows you he needs and wants you, and in the meantime use your other methods of calming him down which are lower down on the levels of responsiveness, such as eye contact and verbal reassurance.

Babies who stand up in the cot will eventually become tired. Roll with resistance, get down to their level so you are face-to-face with them, let them stand for as long as they want, rub their back, pat the mattress and wait for them to sink into your arms or the mattress. By rolling with their resistance you are avoiding the heat of the battle, the stress and strain of trying to get them to lie down. You see we think we need them to lie down as it's a sign for us that they are going to sleep, but if we engage in trying to make them do what they don't want to do then it makes them more resistant, it makes them more awake and it makes us more frustrated. It's all about knowing when to let go, knowing when your actions are helping or hindering sleep. Charm your baby and roll with resistance.

Mirroring behaviour

Your baby is designed to follow your lead, that's how he learns. You smile, he smiles; you frown, he frowns. He learns from your non-verbal communication and what you say. From the minute they are born our babies have the capacity to copy, mimic and mirror our responses and emotions. So use this to help your baby establish a healthy sleeping habit. If you want your baby to lie down, you lie down and show him. If you want your baby to be calm, you must first be calm, tilt your head, speak slower and calmly. Use mirroring behaviour to let your child know what he should do once he is in his cot. You may feel a little silly at first but when you see how well your child responds to your actions you will keep doing it until he gets the message. Smile when your baby is tearful; try to demonstrate the emotion and behaviour you desire in your child.

Functional behaviour

This is about doing what works but with a purpose. This means you can rock your baby, hold him or let your baby suck until he is calm. You can use these tools to help your baby soothe, but you only do it for as long as he needs you to. Once he is calm you stop. Remember your job is to calm your baby and teach him to self-soothe. Self-soothing is all about what he does once he is calm. You have demonstrated your love connection (bonding tool) by responding to his initial need (his crying); now he is calm it's up to him to do the next bit – in this case it's the falling asleep part. Lie him down once he is calm. If he is still a little resistant to being put down, hold him and be still, get him used to being in your arms without movement first. Once he settles you can move to the next step and lie him down. While doing this ensure that you pick up your baby no more than twice to avoid getting caught in a PU/PD cycle, work through your different levels of responsiveness giving each level an opportunity to calm your baby before you move 'up' to the next level. Every response you do with your baby along with your presence should only be done once your baby needs it, and when he doesn't you stop or leave. This will allow your child to learn how to self-soothe and provide you with your exit strategy so that you do not become stuck in the room.

Distraction

This is an effective way of interrupting your baby's distress. The way you distract, though, is key. Most parents are very good at distracting their children in the day by showing them the car, or looking out the window or using sound and light in some way to move their child from one state to the next. It can be very powerful as it means our children who were once unsettled and unhappy forget all about their distress and become engrossed in the new distraction. Parents can feel very smug at this point because they have quite skilfully managed to limit their child's distress.

We need to do the same thing when our children become upset at bedtime, however with one very small yet distinct difference: our distraction techniques need to be in line with sleep. So not only do they need to divert our baby's attention away from crying, but they also have to promote sleep. Here's how to do it in a very functional and love-connected fashion:

* When patting your child's back or their mattress, change the rhythm, pause, resume
* When rocking, change the rhythm, pause, resume
* When verbally reassuring or singing, change the rhythm pattern, pause, resume

Some parents may turn on the light or move their child out of the room. This can be quite damaging to building the sleep pattern as the light creates a more wakeful state and moving the child out of the room makes the child think that the room is a bad place and he may develop a negative association with his room and his cot. We really don't want this: we don't want to send the message that their room, sleep and cot are all bad things. So stay in his room, create a positive association to it by staying in there until he calms down. Use distraction to charm your baby back to sleep.

Touch

Touch is very important for us as human beings and it is a way of communicating that transcends speech and language. Our babies can pick up a lot from being held – they feel safe, they feel love – and it's an amazing love glue. By simply being near our babies we can calm them and send them lots of love messages. There are many ways we can touch our babies and it's important to know that we are sending the right message when we do: we can hold our babies, massage our babies and pat, rock and stroke them. Each type of touch can and does send a different message to our young. Newborn babies are extremely sensitive to touch and research suggests that gentle or light stroking can make them feel uncomfortable at best and anxious at worst. It is advisable, therefore, that we touch our very new babies firmly, hold them firmly and swaddle them firmly, so that they feel snug and we override the Moro reflex that can startle and frighten them. Holding your baby's head and chest, and patting him can all help to make him feel reassured.

Skin-to-skin

The power of skin-to-skin in calming your baby should not be overlooked. Skin-to-skin helps to reduce stress levels (cortisol hormones) that are produced when your baby cries. Your warmth and skin-to-skin contact can help your baby soothe quickly and efficiently. When this happens you are aiding your baby's emotional brain development, which will help to create a calmer and more secure child as he grows and develops.

When you hold your baby use cheek-to-cheek as your skin is soft, your baby will be able to feel you, smell you and you can breathe gently in his ear. If you are laying your baby on a flat surface or on a bed you can easily kneel down and offer cheek-to-cheek contact with your baby to help him soothe. When your baby is in the cot, get your face as close to the bars as you can. Kangaroo your baby when they become very distressed – this means placing them on your bare skin chest-to-chest with their bare skin; this is the ultimate love bonding and is the highest level of responsiveness we can give. It is perfectly acceptable for you to calm your baby in this way and once calm place your baby down. Very new babies may inadvertently fall asleep on you and this may be very difficult to avoid. I would suggest that you get yourself into the pattern of calming your baby in this way and placing him down once he is asleep so when your baby is able to stretch being awake for longer periods you are already in the habit of responding to him in this way. The kangaroo care approach came about in the 1970s. When looking into care for premature babies, researchers found that babies who were held close to their mothers' bodies for large portions of the day not only survived, but thrived. There are numerous benefits from kangaroo care that include psychical benefits, feeding benefits, and sleeping benefits. The gains and benefits – decreased crying, regular breathing pattern and stable heart rate – can also be felt by babies born at full term. Benefits for parents have been noted as more milk production, more confidence in parenting and increased bonding and attachment.

Put them down

For your baby who is six months or younger, when you put your baby down to keep them asleep and/or calm, you should try to reduce the impact of the tilt reflex. Our babies are a bundle of reflex movements this early on and so moving them in a particular way can prompt a reflex. Lying them down in their cot is one of those movements, which means that our baby's eyes, arms and hands will open in a startled response. To avoid and limit this reflex put them down feet first and let their head be the last to go on the mattress. Babies who go into a sleeping position or lying position from our arms are more likely to wake due to the 'tilt' reflex. Older babies can be placed in the cot feet first as well and as they have more control and are more awake at this phase the putting down in the cot should be done with them facing us and awake for at least 10 minutes.

Pick up/put down

This is often referred to as Tracy Hogg's PU/PD and is a way of calming your baby through touch and holding: calming him in your arms and then placing him back down when he is calm. This is a very effective way of soothing your baby and follows the principles of functional behaviour. In the fourth trimester, the three months after birth where your baby requires a lot of touch and skin-to-skin from you, the PU/PD method is a good way of helping your baby learn to soothe and prepares your baby for sleep. I would recommend the use of PU/PD between the ages of 0–12 weeks. At around four months your baby is learning to move and find his own idiosyncratic way of falling asleep; this is an opportunity to teach your baby to settle in his space allowing him at least 10–15 minutes of snuggling – down time on his own. Using PU/PD with an older child can cause them to become more distressed and prolong the sleeping process. Therefore parents should really only use PU/PD with babies who are less than four months of age. This advice is contrary to what Tracy talks about in her books. However, having worked with thousands of parents it has become clear to me and my parents that after three months babies become more distressed when the PU/PD method is used. My aim is to help babies sleep but also limit distress for parent and baby. Older babies do not respond well to being picked up and then put back down as they get confused and distressed. The message they may get is that they are being rescued by being held and then abandoned once put back down. The aim of my method is to help babies learn that they are safe in their cot and that they can be calmed within their cot and there is no need for them to be rescued as they are safe.

Movement

Use movement functionally, whether your baby is in your arms or in her bed. Move her to calm her by rocking, swaying, or when in the cot you can use movement by what I call the bum shuffle rock. Gently move your baby's bum from side to side, this can be done with your baby lying on her back and parents scooping their hands underneath their baby and between her legs, and while holding on to the nappy rock back and forth until your baby is calm. Movement initially is a good distraction tool for calming distressed babies. The movement also works at replicating the womb where your baby experienced movement all the time. Movement is an excellent tool to calm and reassure your baby.

Deep breathe, don't 'shh'

Deep breathing in your baby's ear is just as effective as white noise, if not more. Try to avoid 'shhing' your baby as this can become more violent if done frequently and loudly. The other drawback is that shhing involves your stomach muscles and when you shh you become tense; the more you shh the more tense you become. Try it and see what I mean. Now let's take the situation of you trying to calm your baby and the vicious sleep cycle: we do not want to do anything that increases our negative experiences, we are already anxious and tense, so shhing will make that worse. Deep breathing, on the other hand, is a wonderful calming action as it soothes our babies and us too. It is virtually impossible to be tense and deep breathe at the same time. So, as I say to all my parents, let go of the shhing and deep breathe instead and feel the difference and see the impact you will have.

Pre-emptive feeding

Simply put, a pre-empt feed is a feed that you do before a baby wakes up and cries. These can also be known as dream feeds. Feeding can be a tricky activity for some parents, and deciding how and when to schedule feeding can be a minefield. Whatever your routine, feeding your baby should be done in a calm and cosy environment, and you should make the experience as comfortable for you as it is for your child. Feed your child well before he goes down to sleep.

Ensure your first pre-emptive feed will be around 10pm for a baby that is asleep by seven. For babies who are on a different bedtime schedule their next feed should be 3–4 hours after their bedtime feed. Try to feed before your baby wakes up: we want to feed our babies before the hunger sends a signal to their brain that it needs to wake up, thus disturbing the body rhythm. We don't want to have this trigger become a habit because over time your baby's body rhythm will think that it is okay to wake at this time, so even when your baby no longer needs the feed the body clock will automatically wake him. Dream feeding or pre-emptive feeding will ensure that you can feed your baby when he is still asleep and maintain a healthy sleeping habit. Parents who are breastfeeding or feeding on demand may not find this option feasible in the early months of their baby's life, but as your little one gets older and the spaces between the feeds widen, you may find that pre-empting their feeding at night is a helpful way for you all as a family to manage the sleep.

> Nutritionally, breastfeeding is best for babies, but breastfed babies do probably wake more often for feeds. We can counteract the body rhythm being unsettled by this with dream feeds.

Transitional object

A transitional object is anything that our babies are attached to that helps them to self-soothe and fall asleep. If your baby is attached to touching your skin or your hair, you may want to find a transitional object that replicates what your baby gets from you through their senses of this touch and feeling, such as a muslin or dummy. The golden key here is to ground it in your smell, make it smell of you, so wear the item down your chest for a few hours or wash it with your shampoo. For a child that is not overly enamoured by a transitional object we can still get them to accept it by grounding it in smell.

Most parents just present the transitional object when it's bedtime. This is only part of the answer. We need to ground attachment to the object in every opportunity we get throughout the day. This is achieved by presenting it whenever your child has a strong reaction (good or bad), or whenever you hold, comfort or love your baby. You should present the object and get them to touch, hold, smell and feel it. You may at first have to just have it with you and your baby just has it in his line of sight. The idea here is that he will transfer the same feelings of love on the object because he recognises it as being part of the message you send him when you comfort him. You are assisting in helping your baby to associate being calmed by you and the object and over time he will see the object and become calm naturally. When this learning occurs it's the perfect opportunity to present the object at night as a tool to help charm, calm and soothe your angel to sleep.

When introducing a transitional object to your infant's world please ensure you think about safety, making sure there are no small dangerous detachable parts that can be swallowed or cause harm, and ensure the fibres are breathable. There is no age limit to a transitional object, as these can be introduced by way of emotional attachment as described above. Parents may also want to consider having a back-up that is safely stored and also ensuring key members of the family that you visit frequently have the same transitional object so you don't need to take it out of the house.

Attachment tools for children aged 2+

- Give toddlers clear explanations, state the facts, remind them and repeat, give them a time and warn them when the time is reducing to prepare them for change.
- Give lots of positive praise and be patient.
- Acknowledge their pain and fear as real.
- Do what you say and mean it.
- Be consistent.
- Work as a team and avoid parental splitting.

- To keep a child engaged change things a bit, it's what I call 'keeping the game alive'.
- Give them short- and long-term goals.
- Give them a sense of ownership of their room and space. This can be achieved by getting them to change the position of furniture, remove or add things and spending more time alone playing in their room outside of bedtime.
- Create a sense of achievement with verbal and non-verbal praise and sticker charts.
- Get him involved in his bedtime routine, get him to pack his own bedtime box, ask him questions about what comes next in the bedtime sequence of events routine.

Your body language

Be mindful of what you are communicating with your body language – be open, responsive and make eye contact. If you are not able to embody that for whatever reason, then this is okay, step away, give yourself some space and time and come back when you are feeling more balanced and able to communicate your love and soothe your child into a calm state. If you have to leave your baby alone and he is unsettled, ensure you have left pieces of you behind, your smell and/or your voice playing on the recording so he doesn't feel alone. If you have another pair of hands and support at home ask them to take over for you for a while to give you a chance to compose yourself.

Your voice

Use your voice to reassure and soothe your baby. Your voice is the last and lowest level of responsiveness and this is what we want our babies to get used to – we want them to be soothed by just our voice so that we can be in another room, or over the baby monitor and just simply say, 'It's okay, it's just sleep', and have our babies respond to that. When you are at that stage then you are doing extremely well. When you no longer have to go into the room, use your presence and/or touch to resettle your child. When just your voice will do, your baby is learning to sleep well.

Get in the cot

It's far better to get into your baby's cot than it is to take him out of the room, or into your bed. I have climbed into many a cot in my days as a hands-on sleep consultant. I would soothe babies in their environment for two reasons, firstly to let them know that where he is is safe and that he does not need to be rescued, and secondly it's a lot easier for me to leave the cot than it is for me to put a baby I have settled and calmed in my arms down into a cot. Most families will see that by getting into the cot they are leaving pieces of themselves behind – their smell for instance – and thus creating a positive association for their child in his cot. You are sending the message that it is okay to be here and your child will grow to love his space.

Once he accepts his cot you can limit the number of times you need to get in as this transference can happen very quickly, usually over one or two nights. Your baby may be happy for you to leave once he is calm, though with other babies you may have to stay until he is asleep. You can do this for up to three days as this will give your baby enough time to get used to the new environment; after this time you can leave your baby when he is calm. Carefully climb out of the cot on the side that your baby is not sleeping on.

Gradual retreat

My version of gradual retreat is to be led by your baby. My plan and method is not based on the length of time you stay in one position but more about how calm your baby is and how safe he feels about moving to the next stage of the process. Once your baby accepts the transitional object or by you leaving pieces of you behind, then he is less likely to be concerned that you are withdrawing. However, should your baby request verbally and non-verbally that you stay in the room then I would use my levels of reassurance tools here to calm him and continue the process of your exit. Wait for him to become calm and then distance yourself or leave.

Most parents have heard of this method and there are varying forms of how you approach this. Essentially you are preparing your child for your exit, so you may increase the distance between you and their bed, you may leave the door open and get closer and closer to the door as the weeks go along. Gradual retreat is not a stand-alone method of sleep training. If your baby is used to having you in the room, he needs to feel safe and secure and have grounding tools in the room as 'replacements' of you. And these replacements and changes to his environment must be acceptable to him. Once you have implemented these changes and you have 'left pieces of you behind' then you can begin your retreat out of his room in a gradual way. This can be done over several nights or several weeks depending on your child's temperament and how quickly he learns to self-soothe. Don't rush the process as this may cause your baby to become more anxious and set you back a few steps.

Chireal's Tip Bits

Your are your child's mirror: what you think and feel is what he will feel.

Our job is to build up the trust and bond with our children and the easiest way to do that is to be truthful and authentic, manage their expectations and don't ever, ever trick them. We want them to trust that we will always return and so when we are planning our gradual retreat from their room we have to maintain their feelings of safety. If you are leaving when he is awake then tell him you are just going out the door and do this for a few moments and return before he calls out for you. It's very important – another golden key here – that you return before he becomes anxious. In order for our children to learn to feel safe we need to override the anxiety trigger. We return back into the room before our babies get anxious. We repeat this step, and as we repeat this step we increase the length of time we are outside the room. Always tell your child that he is safe and you will return, and for babies who have not acquired language use your body language and repetitive behaviour to demonstrate that you will always come back.

Your child should be feeling calm and secure in any event as you have left lots of pieces of you behind in his room and he has built up, because of you, a positive attachment to his space. So you tell him you are popping to the loo, or to check on a sibling or Daddy, and return before he calls out for you. Over time your child will build up a tolerance to being in his room alone, because he has become used to it, and because he knows that you will always come back, because he trusts you and you have been truthful and honest and kept your word. This is your exit strategy. The long-term goal is for you to be able to leave the room and come back only to check on your baby.

It's worth noting that some cautious babies may find it hard to tolerate your absence for very long. I would advise in this instance to lay the foundation with your child in the day first, play lots of peek-a-boo games where you 'disappear' for only a few seconds and increase the time you are 'gone' for. This will help your child become less anxious as he will see your leaving as okay and your return as a positive thing.

If your baby already has a comforter or transitional object and stills requires you then this is a sign that your baby is anxious and that perhaps you need to go back to changing your responses to your baby in the day, as this may be a clear sign that your baby has not acquired this learning point and that you may have started your plan too soon, before you were able to lay down the foundation.

CASE STUDY

Background

Marcia is a woman in her late forties; she is a full-time mum and has returned back to work after six months' maternity leave, She had recently separated from her husband who no longer lives with them. She contacted me one month before returning to work as she wanted to help her son Ollie get into a healthy sleeping habit in the day and night. Marcia informed me that her parents would be helping with child care in the day and she had negotiated flexible working from home two days a week and therefore her son being able to sleep well both during the day and at night would be hugely beneficial.

Marcia explained that her son was a fretful baby and would cry often and therefore she would manage his distress by carrying and holding him. This extended to carrying and holding him when he was calm. She also told me that he would fall asleep on her chest and once asleep she would place him in his cot and then rest while he slept. Ollie's cot was in Marcia's bedroom and Marcia explained that she would like him to stay sleeping with her for a few more months. Ollie is currently still breastfed but Marcia would like him to be able to take the bottle as she would like to express milk when she is at work and continue breastfeeding when she is at home. Ollie wakes frequently during the night and at varying times. Marcia hasn't been able to establish a feeding pattern yet. During the day, Ollie only sleeps for 30 minutes and feeds and wakes frequently at night. Marcia's parenting style is authoritative.

Ollie

Ollie had a natural delivery after a straightforward pregnancy; there were no significant events to note about his birth. Ollie initially struggled to latch on when breastfeeding and Marcia had support from a lactation consultant, which was successful. Ollie breastfed for four months and during his breastfeeding time he would prefer the left breast. He would demonstrate this preference by becoming unsettled when placed on the right breast and feeding well when placed on the breast he liked the most. Ollie most enjoys the time when he is close to his mum, he does not tolerate being held by others, and spends most of his time being cuddled.

Problem

As Ollie is a fretful baby he will need to be eased into change gradually as change made too suddenly may cause him to become distressed. Ollie is at an age where it is expected that he is close to his mother and developmentally it is what is the most helpful. Marcia having to go back to work means that the problem is about helping Ollie to feel safe with another caregiver, in this situation his grandparents. To help Ollie sleep without falling asleep on Mum and on the breast is currently his sleep problem as, due to dependency on his mother's actions, he is unable to put himself back off to sleep when he wakes after a nap or during the night. The other issue is to also work with Ollie and Marcia so that Ollie begins to accept a bottle of his mother's expressed milk.

Initially Marcia had intended staying at home for a year and so it has taken her some time to adjust to the fact that she has to return back to work sooner than she had hoped. This meant that she was feeling a bit low in mood at times and had natural worries about missing her son while she was at work and fears around being a good parent and balancing the challenges of work. She felt that she had the support of her parents and felt lucky that she would be leaving her son with her parents as opposed to someone outside of her family or having to pay for care. This she felt helped ease some of the discomfort around her return to work.

Ollie's problem cycle

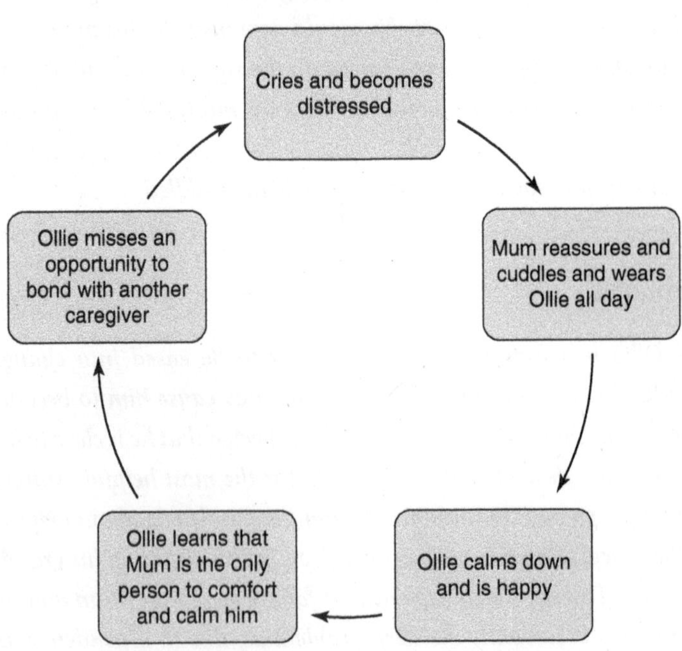

Marcia's problem cycle

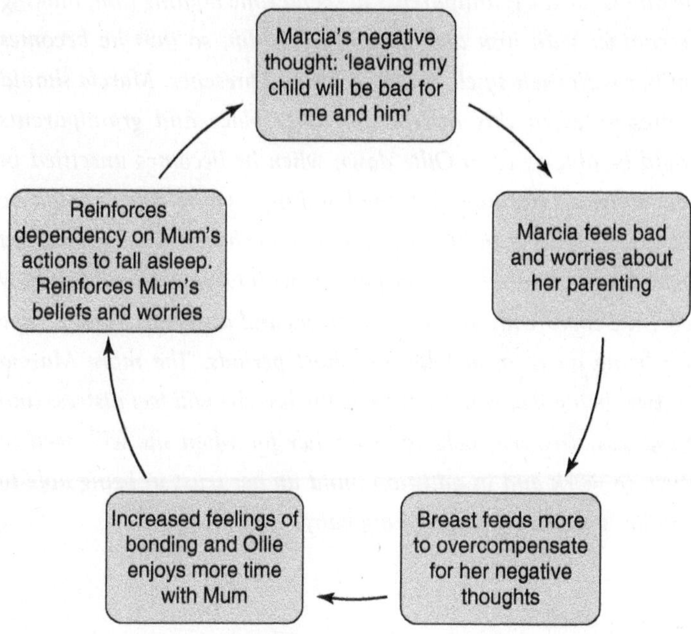

Plan

My plan was to begin to build a relationship bond and attachment with Ollie and his grandparents, then to use this growing relationship to help with acceptance of the bottle. I then needed to work with Marcia on her negative thoughts to lift her mood and change the way she looked at her situation, and then finally provide strategies for Marcia and Ollie to work on the sleep and settling.

Action point 1

I advised Marcia that the grandparents should visit at least three times a week and spend time interacting with Ollie, gradually introducing themselves to him by presence first, sound, then touch and then holding. The time in each mode should be gradually increased. The aim is for the grandparents to spend time holding him, making eye contact with him and talking with him, so that he becomes familiar with their smell, touch, voice and presence. Marcia should be present when this interaction takes place and grandparents should be able to calm Ollie down when he becomes unsettled in order for us to test how well the bonding is going. Ollie should be able to accept his grandparents after a week; however, on the second week Marcia should leave her parents with Ollie, this will test how well Ollie copes with his new caregivers and also help Marcia cope with being away from Ollie for short periods. The more Marcia practises being separate from Ollie the less she will feel distress and or sadness. This will help to ready her for when she will need to return to work and in addition build up her trust in being able to leave her parents with her young baby.

Action point 2

In the second week, Ollie's grandparents should begin getting Ollie used to the bottle when they are spending time with him. A small amount of milk should be placed in the bottle and fed to Ollie. The success of taking to the bottle is not gauged by how much he drinks but rather if he is able to suck on it. Grandparents to wear muslin that smells of Mum or Mum's milk over their shoulder and across their chest while feeding Ollie. They should habituate Ollie to the bottle by having the bottle visible around the house.

They should place water in the bottle and feed Ollie water in between breastfeeds. Only grandparents should use the bottle with Ollie.

Action point 3

I helped Marcia challenge her automatic thoughts and use more helpful and balanced thoughts that would allow her to be more accepting of her current situation and successful in changing how she responds to Ollie in order to help him sleep at night.

Marcia needs to use statements that are more helpful such as: 'I am a good mother, I will be spending four days a week with my child and at work for three days. I will be home more than I am away. My parents are more than acceptable attachment figures for my son. I will not miss out on watching my son grow. Things may be hard but I will cope.'

Action point 4

In the first week Marcia is to leave pieces of herself around the room, so that Ollie can feel, see and smell her even if she is not present. Pictures of Marcia's face, muslins that she has worn down her chest for a while so it smells of her and her breast milk. Marcia should record her voice singing or reading a story. Marcia should begin placing Ollie on the floor or in a seat looking directly at her and talking and playing with him instead of holding him. This will create space and distance so that Ollie can become used to lying and sitting on his own. Marcia to play peek-a-boo games and leave the room for short periods and come back in an animated fashion so that Ollie smiles and learns that Mum will always come back and that when she returns he feels good rather than being sad that she has left. To further enhance the work of separateness, I asked Marcia to begin to leave the room but remain within Ollie's earshot, talk to him continually and return before he became distressed.

Marcia to take Ollie off the breast before he falls asleep, using split-feeding at night.

Action point 5

In the second week Marcia is to work on settling at night, placing Ollie to fall asleep next to her for three days instead of on top of her or while breastfeeding. Ollie learns that he can fall asleep in a place away from his mum but also have her nearby. Once asleep, Marcia should place him in his cot and use different levels of intervention to calm him should he become unsettled.

Feeds should be structured every four hours, introducing a dream feed at 10pm, feed at 2am and 6am. It's not a problem if Ollie falls asleep on the breast during night-time feeds, all wakes to be managed using different levels of interventions.

To work on daytime naps, Ollie should be settled in the same way. Resettle for 10 minutes only if Ollie woke at 30 minutes. Once Ollie is able to learn to sleep on his own the length of his daytime naps will lengthen naturally as when he goes through light sleep he will know what to do to move to the next phase of the sleep cycle without his mother's actions.

In the third week Marcia should place Ollie in his cot awake after split feed and use levels of intervention in a functional way, such as the bum rock and holding his chest until he is calm and then allowing him to fall asleep.

In the fourth week Marcia is to use gradual retreat to allow Ollie to fall asleep on his own and without her presence. Once Ollie is calm, she should wait ten minutes and then leave the room and wait outside the room, leaving the sound of her voice playing or reading stories on the CD so that Ollie doesn't feel alone. Also leaving her smell in the cot on the sheets.

Action point 6

Week 5 – Marcia is to monitor progress and keep thought diary. She should focus on remaining consistent. If Ollie becomes upset or distressed, go back a few steps and get him used to the changes slowly and gradually. Use grounding tools to help him feel safe and secure and orient him in time and space.

Outcome

It took Ollie a bit longer than a week to get used to his grandparents' care and build a significant relationship with them, which slowed down the plan a little. But it was done at a pace that Marcia was happy with and it meant that Ollie was not in distress. Ollie took to the bottle successfully and allowed only his grandmother to feed him. This was something that Marcia felt she and her mother could live with. Marcia was able to lift her mood with the use of self-affirming balanced statements and she was also able to feel okay about leaving Ollie for short periods of time, which meant she felt a little more hopeful that returning to work would not be as bad as she imagined or too detrimental to her relationship with her son.

Ollie struggled a little with the split feed and this meant that Marcia found she sometimes had to allow him to close his eyes and relax before she took the nipple from his mouth. She found feeding him when he was naked really worked as it meant that while she got him dressed he was awake and she could place him down to sleep awake.

Ollie settled well at night in the first week and took to falling asleep next to his mum well. He still woke the same number of times but was easier to settle. The second week of placing Ollie in the cot awake was a lot harder for Marcia and she found she had to alternate between cuddling him and putting him down in his cot. The third week was more successful and Ollie was settling on his own in his cot with Marcia present.

By week 6 Ollie was able to sleep through the night and take regular feeds and settle back without issue and was sleeping for an hour and sometimes more for his naps during the day.

So we have reached the stage in the plan where we are now pulling together what you know about shaping your baby's sleeping patterns. You now have the behavioural tools you need and you know how to use them for success. You have identified your barriers to success and worked on managing your emotions and thinking styles to be in the right position to effect change and help your baby establish a natural and nurturing sleep pattern. In order for us to pull the plan together we need to also address learning your baby's language, I have mentioned your child's temperament and for some newborn parents it may be harder to know in the first few weeks what their temperament is, so for all newborn parents and to aid parents with older babies I have addressed the issue on knowing and learning your child's language by being able to read their behaviour. This will allow you to devise your plan more appropriately for your family as you will know exactly what your child needs and you are less likely to confuse your baby's needs with your fears. I am hoping to assist you here, so that you are more confident in knowing what your child's needs are and what your needs are so that you can successfully and confidently put your plan into action.

Chapter 9

Creating your individual sleep plan

Did you know: Just as some people talk in their sleep, sign language speakers have been known to sign in their sleep?

YOU NOW HAVE ALL THE KNOWLEDGE ABOUT READING YOUR child's behaviour and insight into what your baby's sleep issue is. You know which tools you will need to help calm, soothe and settle your baby and you have adapted your environment and your child's environment ready for sleep. You have identified your barriers to success and have managed your thoughts and emotions – you are now skilful at staying in the moment and not being distracted by your strong negative thoughts and emotions. You now have your completed formulation. What is left now is for you to devise a sleep plan based on your child's temperament and your family's needs.

This plan will be unique to you and your family. It will take you where you need to be – the beautiful land of gorgeous, glorious sleep for you all. This plan is a plan that will work. We have looked at your child's needs, your needs and we have figured out what the problem is, as well as what keeps it going. Now we are moving on to the most exciting part! We are about to break that cycle. With this plan we are going to solve your child's sleep problem.

Chireal's Tip Bits

Keep a log of your baby's sleep a week prior to starting the plan so that you have a comparison.

Let's start with a reminder about sleep. Sleep and what good sleep is, is just as much about perception and feeling than actual fact. What I mean is, if we think we have had a bad night's sleep, or our child has not slept well when actually they have slept for eight hours, the mere fact that we believe we have not slept well will make us feel bad or inadequate and contribute to our vicious cycle of on-going poor sleep. It may be a perception but perception is reality – it's your experience. To make the right changes you need to get as objective a view of the sleep situation as possible. Therefore, you need to take this into account when devising your sleep plan; you need to know exactly how much sleep your baby is actually getting. This is key for many reasons: it's important to keep an eye on your baby's sleeping pattern so you know where she is at. You also need to know how much sleep you want them to have. This is your goal. If your baby is sleeping only five hours in the night and you would like them to sleep for seven, your goal is seven hours. You need to improve your child's sleep by two hours. You need to keep your eye on the overall goal – this is the only way you can travel to your destination.

Design your sleep diary

The easiest way to monitor your progress is to keep a sleep diary. Your sleep diary will be your road map. By examining your sleep diary you will be able to look at what is actually happening, what is working and what is still left for you to work on. I will charge you with keeping a log of your child's sleep, as well as your comments on your actions for bedtime and naps. Take a quick look at the example sleep diary below; here you will see that there are several columns for you to fill in about when your child woke, when they fell asleep, how long it took you to settle your child and what you did. (See Appendix 1 for an example of a sleep diary pre-plan, and for weeks 1 and 2 of the plan.)

	Date/Day of week						
	Monday	Tuesday	Wednesday	Thursday	Friday	Saturday	Sunday
Time baby went to bed	19.45	20.12	19.40	19.30	19.35	19.30	19.15
Time s/he woke	21.00	22.00	21.30	21.15	none	none	none
Time went to sleep	21.05	22.05	21.35	21.16	N/A	N/A	N/A
Time s/he woke	01.57	23.30 01.20	02.00	01.30	02.10	02.05	N/A
Time went to sleep	02.00	23.47 01.30	02.05	01.37	02.15	02.07	N/A
Time(s) woke in the night	2	3	2 Awake at 06.15	2	1	1	0
What you did	Patted, reassured, picked up	Pick up and deep breathing in his ear. Fed at midnight	Presence. Verbal reassurance	Presence. Baby self-settled	Presence. Verbal reassurance	Presence only	Nothing
Comment	In the room hands on with lots of cuddles	Felt confident to just hold and be calm	Dream fed at 10pm	Just waited by the door	He cried a little and moaned, but I spoke softly from the doorway		He stirred in the night and I could hear him but he resettled on his own

It's very important that you record what you have done to settle your baby so that we can review which of your actions work and which need attention. It's also important to fill in all the columns as we are going to measure 'change'.

Now here is another one of those golden keys coming up: how we measure change. If your child wakes 15 times a night, you might look at your sleep diary and think measuring change is just about reducing the number of wakes. You would be right, but that isn't the whole answer. You may look at the diary's last column (number of wakes) and see that as the only indicator for change. That sort of 'change' is what I refer to as a 'macro-change' – a big change. But our behaviour also changes in small ways – 'micro-changes'. We need to be aware of what these micro-changes in behaviour are as they are essential, if not imperative, indicators that what we are doing is actually working. It helps us to be aware of these micro-changes so that if we don't see macro-changes happening we still remain focused and with our eye firmly fixed on our end goal.

In the first week or two of your sleep plan, you may not see a macro-change which you may expect to look like the number of wakes reducing or your baby waking for 20 minutes and then dramatically waking for 5 minutes, but there will be lots of micro-changes, which is more realistic and natural and what I have come to use as a motivational guide for my parents. This too will help to keep you confident, motivated and on track. There is a saying: 'it's not the elephant that will get you but the ants'. Sometimes if we focus on the big obvious changes to sleep we miss the small subtle changes, become unfocused and give the plan up. I want to help you to use your plan to notice the macro-changes and the micro-changes.

So where on the sleep diary can you measure your micro-changes? The column 'time woke' and 'time back to sleep' is where you will find the micro-changes in your child's sleeping pattern. In our example you can see that our baby woke first at 9pm after an hour and 15 minutes of sleep. Mum gave verbal reassurance, patted and picked up baby and baby was asleep at 9.05pm. This tells us that it took Mum five minutes to help baby settle and baby was only awake for five minutes. The next time baby woke at 01.57 baby was asleep by 2am. Now we are going to look at the length of time baby was awake for – the first time it was five minutes, the second it was three minutes. This tells us something very important; it tells us that baby is getting used to being soothed and is learning to fall asleep. This is what we call a micro-change – we are looking for the length of time a baby is awake for to reduce. This will probably be what we see more of in the first two weeks of a sleep plan, where your baby is learning how to fall asleep independently, how to join up her body rhythm and is getting used to being soothed in new ways.

Now you know all the things your baby has to learn and unlearn, signs of these changes will be seen in places you may not have been looking, i.e. the time it takes for your baby to fall asleep each time she wakes is where we look to know if our babies are learning all the things we need them to learn. This is why we may still see our babies waking for the same number of times each night but as she learns and as her body rhythm works with us the time she is awake gradually begins to reduce. When this happens we know we are working effectively on our child's body rhythm, dependency or anxiety issue.

Now let's take a look at the sleep diary again. As you can see, we start to see that the parent does not have to always pick the baby up each time she wakes. What is happening here is that the parent is allowing the child to self-settle – they are doing this by using PAUSE and the varying levels of response. The baby then learns that her needs will be met and she does not need to feel anxious because she can feel and know her parent's presence. Because she feels safe, she is less likely to call or cry out. This time allows for you as parent to be present in the room but use the right level of response in order to help your baby soothe herself to sleep. In the example diary you can see that by Wednesday the parent only needs to be in the room and verbally reassure. Again, this small yet significant change tells us a lot: the time it takes baby to fall asleep is shortening and the type of contact that the parent has with the baby is also lessening. This tells us that the plan is working. Yes, the parent is still awake and is still in the room and so for some this may still feel like hard work because 'your' sleep is still being disrupted. But remember, knowing that you are on the right track and that you are still teaching your baby to fall asleep will keep you motivated. Know that as soon as your baby begins to sleep well at night-time, so will you – these helpful thoughts and the overwhelming evidence of your baby's micro-changes will keep you moving in the direction of success. On our example diary you will see that by Sunday baby is settling herself and the parent is no longer in the room.

Keep in mind that when you come to the end of your four-to-six-week plan, you will have a child that has learnt to soothe, sleep and settle without your intervention. This will be a long-term, long-standing natural sleep pattern that can be maintained with your assistance by controlling the environment and your responses. This all equals sleep success!

Your sleep diary will be your road map that will help you get to your destination of good sleep. It's important that you refer back to your road map so you can see what changes are happening to keep you heading in the right direction.

As your child needs less intervention from you, you will work through the different levels of intervention and gradually grade down your attention, so you are only giving your child the bare minimum to help them soothe and focus on sleep. The last thing you will be doing will be giving verbal reassurance (see page 150–51).

Example of personalised sleep plans

UNDERLYING SLEEP PROBELM	CONSEQUENCE	UNIQUE PLAN/ACTION
ANXIETY	Clinginess. Cries often when parents leave alone	Ground child in sight, sound and smell. Adapt environment, use responsive parenting to help settle and resettle
DEPENDENT	Will not sleep without rocking, bottle, parents' actions	Introduce a transitional object, create a structured bedtime routine and use consistency
SLEEP CYCLE	Wakes at the same time, difficult to go to sleep. Wakes early	Routine, consistency, use props and cues. Use gradual retreat and responsive parenting

When to start your sleep plan

Ideally you should start your sleep plan when you know you have at least two weeks clear of major activity, such as a holiday or relatives coming to stay or a particularly busy week that is unusual from your normal week. While this plan works if you are travelling, it is best that you allow yourself and your family some space and time to get used to the new sleep plan. The families I have worked with over the years have found it helpful to start on the weekend, usually a Friday. This gives them the opportunity to relax and not have to worry about the normal time restrictions you may have in the week, like work, school runs, and so on. You also have the opportunity to enlist help and support that might otherwise be unavailable in the week, and you also have the chance to rest and regroup.

Changing your behaviour patterns is hard and responding to your child in a way that breaks your habits will take some thinking and consideration, so it's important that you give yourself and your family the best chance of success. Babies and children are usually a lot more adaptable to change and cope with things a lot more easily than adults do. Knowing this will allow you to approach this sleep plan with more confidence because the hurdle you have to overcome is a lot lower and simpler than you think. I want to take each step, each stage and each milestone one day at a time, one moment at a time; there is no rush and there is nothing you can do that will be disastrous. Every opportunity is a golden moment to learn from so we can use this to our benefit the next day. Everything you do with your child will give you more and more information, therefore I want you to feel comfortable and confident that even if things don't go according to plan, you will get back on track.

When you start changing your baby's behaviour, each night you will record what happens and what you do in your sleep diary. Each morning you will revive your sleep diary and think about what you did well and how your baby responded. Each day you will think about what you need to do the next night and what you may need to do differently.

Use what you know about yourself and your child to keep moving forward towards your goal. You may find that you are attempting to rock your baby functionally and she falls asleep in your arms. Your milestone or your next action point for the following night will simply be to rock functionally and aim to lay your child down, feet first in the cot, before she falls asleep. Should your baby start to become unsettled when you start to place her down or once she is in the cot you should use the level 4 of reassurance, which is to use skin-to-skin, cheek-to-cheek comfort while leaning into the cot and/or resettle her from within the cot using verbal reassurance and touch at level 3 of reassurance.

If you use the dummy, breast or bottle to soothe and your baby falls asleep on it the second night, your aim for the next night is to take them off a little sooner. Use every situation as an opportunity to learn, improve and modify. Be brave, take risks, your child will be okay because you are there nurturing her, loving her and sending her the message that she is okay, with you and without you. Never forget that it is your baby's job to fall asleep and your job to provide the right environment and facilitate the process.

Fill in your sleep diary for a week and after 2–3 days you will begin to see change and improvement. You will see that your baby is responding to your new behaviour. Use this to decide if you are ready to move on to your next milestone or if you need to stay at this stage a little longer just so that your baby gets used to things and learns, for example, how to put their dummy back in or accepts the audio story book you have placed in their room. You can set the pace of how your sleep plan progresses because there is no right or wrong way. As long as you are using PAUSE, the attachment tools and the varying levels of responsiveness you will always be on the right track. Be aware of your negative thoughts and use your mindfulness skills to keep them at bay, remembering not to be led by fear but motivated by confidence.

Recognise your own success

Most of the parents I meet lack confidence. The reason they feel less confident is because they have not seen that what they are doing is working. You may identify with this. In the absence of evidence our brains tell us that we are not successful and this does not make us feel good. We have to turn this around. Confidence comes from the evidence of success. I want to help you regain confidence – that wonderful feeling you feel in your whole body when you put your baby down and she is finally asleep – and we need the evidence of things working to help us trigger that feeling again. I'll let you into a little secret – in order to build up confidence we need to set our goals a lot closer to home. We need small, achievable goals; goals that are not elusive; goals that are easily achieved. This will help us build up our confidence and when our confidence is building up slowly we get stronger and stronger, and the stronger and more confident you are, the more likely you are to succeed. NOW!

If you have an extremely poor sleeper and you wait until she has learned to fall asleep independently before recognising your success, you may end up feeling less confident as the evidence of them not sleeping will far outweigh the evidence of them sleeping well. I need you to look for smaller signs that you are successful, look for the evidence and you will find it. Look for the subtle signs that your baby is responding to you. Remember, your baby is learning too, so if she doesn't get it straight away that's not a reflection on you or your performance, and it most definitely is not a sign of the quality of your parenting.

Signs that you are a success

* The way your baby looks at you
* Your baby's smile
* Reaching out to be with you
* Moving towards your touch
* Your child pausing when you enter a room, speak or touch them
* The way you are with your child during the day
* The way you meet your child's needs
* Your baby thriving
* Your baby's sociable nature

I could go on, but each family is different and your baby will show you in many ways how successful you are; you just need to look for it. Try not to just limit your view to the big signs, like my baby eats and sleeps well. There is so much more in between – the subtle signs that are there waiting for you to recognise them. Use these signs and look at them every day, tell yourself that you are a good-enough parent and the job you are doing is an amazing one. Let that feeling of confidence grow until it is a big ball of confident love, warmth and strength.

Donald Winnicott (1953) talks about the good-enough mother and shaping a child's learning through transitional objects and gradually allowing a child to get used to new concepts in a way that works well for the child and for the mother. These concepts are not new and it is a shame that they appear to have lost momentum. I would like to try to raise the awareness as I believe that his concepts fit very well with my belief and also that he has a very strong message that also is similar to the CBT model of changing how you view yourself and your child and you change your experience. A 'good-enough mother', who learns best how to look after her baby not from health professionals and self-help books but from having been a baby herself. 'She acts naturally, naturally' (Winnicott, 1988). Winnicott argues that mothers are the expert of their babies, and not the so-called expert such as doctors or psychologists. I believe that you are the expert of your family and I am the expert of my model; by creating a synergy between the two we can create a plan that works.

Set achievable goals

When it comes to changing your child's sleeping behaviour, we need to set small, achievable goals. By breaking down the goals into steps (or milestones), it makes it easier for us to succeed.

Milestones (smaller goals)

For my baby to …

* be calm in my arms
* be calmed by her dummy
* be calm without rocking
* take sips from a bottle
* lie in her cot/bed
* be calmed by my voice
* settle well at bedtime
* go back to sleep quickly after waking up
* feed less at night

Bigger, endgame goals

For my baby to …

* fall asleep in the cot
* sleep well at naptime
* sleep well at night
* only wake in the night for feeds

Identify your barriers to success

We all wonder from time to time why something hasn't worked, usually after we have begun the task and then failed in some way. I want us to flip the script here and make sure we know the answer to this question before we start and to ensure we won't fail. I want you to think about what our barriers are to success before we even begin. Here I will share some of the tips, tools and tricks of the trade that psychologists who use the CBT model employ to shape behaviour and to increase the chances of success. Here's another one of what I call my golden keys: I want you to think about what would stop this plan from working. What things, people, behaviours, thoughts and conditions would get in the way of you achieving your goal? What would the road-blocks be to you getting to where you want to be? If we can think of all the things likely to trip us up we can build in backup plans and contingencies to ensure we remain robust, on track and successful.

Here are some examples of potential roadblocks and some potential solutions. Use this example to get you thinking about your barriers to success and then use the form at the back of this book to fill in your own and plan ahead.

Example of potential roadblocks to achieving goal

BARRIERS TO SUCCESS	CONSIDERATIONS	SOLUTION
Parental tiredness	This is a natural position as most sleep-deprived parents will feel tired.	Get as much sleep as you can three days prior to starting the plan. Get other members of the family to support you, like taking alternate nights to take care of the night-time needs of the baby.
One partner absent due to occupational commitments	Some parents feel that they are unable to get into a sleep plan if they are on their own. Help and support is one way of being successful but it's not the only way. By planning and managing your worries and emotions you can do this alone.	Set achievable goals, cancel activities that are non-essential, be organised, have everything you need to hand. Have a routine; ask for help from other family members.

(*continued*)

BARRIERS TO SUCCESS	CONSIDERATIONS	SOLUTION
Booked holidays	Some families think a plan won't work if they go on holiday or they worry the holiday will undo their hard work because of the time zone differences and difference in environment. This is not the case when using our sequence of events approach.	Start the plan two weeks prior to any planned trip. Bring grounding tools (smells, sound, something to hold, even half clean bed sheets that smell of home and are familiar) with you. Follow the time zone of the country you are in immediately. Use sequence of events as your routine to let your child know what to do and when.
Extended family sharing home	Some families have little option than to live with other members of the family and this can be a very useful position, whether it's grandparents or children from previous relationships.	Inform everyone of your plan to shape your baby's sleeping pattern. Give everyone a role to play, small or large, even if it's getting them out of your hair for a few moments. Make people feel useful.
Different aged siblings	It's often hard for parents to know what to do with older siblings when they are putting their baby to bed and hate having to stick them in front of the TV.	If it's safe and age appropriate leave your older child occupied with a task until you return. Give your child a role to play in every aspect of the routine. Have the children in the same room and read stories to them all. Put the older child to bed first.
Worries and thoughts about the plan not working	This is the most common barrier and with a little work you can overcome it.	Believe in yourself, be confident, break the negative cycle and think helpful thoughts. Remember worries aren't facts. Trust that this programme will work.

BARRIERS TO SUCCESS	CONSIDERATIONS	SOLUTION
Problems with babies feeding	Some babies may not take to breast- or bottle-feeding well and may not eat as much as we would like.	Feed your baby little and often. Pre-empt night feeds. Feed more in the day than at night. See a specialist sleep consultant, lactation consultant, GP, paediatrician.
Medical / health conditions Short and long term	Special babies and babies with medical concerns such as reflux will often have difficulty sleeping.	Accept that for now your baby will sleep differently to others, your progress may be slower. Manage the health conditions as a priority; meet the needs of your child first. Things will change.

Measuring your progress

Weeks 1 and 2

In the first week you will see the most change and the sleep diary will provide you with the major and minor changes you will need to assess your progress. When you have two weeks' worth of sleep recording you can then use the contents to see how much your baby has improved. If you have kept a log of your baby's sleeping habits a week prior to starting the sleep programme you will see a vast improvement. By comparing weeks as opposed to comparing changes made day by day you are able to get an overview of your progress that you may not actually feel or notice daily. Below is an example of two weeks compared.

Most parents worry that they won't make any changes to their baby's sleep habits, but it is extremely rare to not make any changes at all if you have been following the gentle sleep system as explained. However, some parents might find that their progress is not as quick as they would like, and illness or other unexpected events can cause the sleep plan to stall. It is important to remember that a problem with sleep is about how your baby is currently sleeping and how you would like your baby to sleep. Sometimes we need to use our child's temperament and stage of development to gauge what she is capable of and how this will impact on her sleep in order for us to have a good idea of what our baby's ideal sleeping pattern will be.

We will discuss these types of situations in detail in the following chapters. The thing to remember now is that by following this plan you will make meaningful and significant changes to your child's sleeping habits.

Weeks 3 and 4 review

As stated, weeks 1 and 2 are where we see the most change and at the end of week 2 we generally get an idea of where we want to be. Weeks 3 and 4 are mainly about maintenance and troubleshooting and ensuring we are embedding the new learning.

Weeks 3 and 4 may look a little like the example below; don't worry so much if yours doesn't as we go back to our saying that all babies are different. This is just an example so that we can look at what's happening.

The CBT model is principally about problem-solving, being able to define where you are and where you would like to be. The journey towards change is not always a smooth one and even with the best will in the world, some parents and babies may experience some difficulty on the four-to-six week gentle sleep solution plan. This by no means reflects on you as the parents but rather on the many variables that exist and it would be unrealistic for us to be able to do it all. We are aiming for good enough here. You have done an amazing job to get this far, to take in all the lessons and apply them, so please remember to congratulate yourself and reward yourself for all your efforts. I want you to be able to be as compassionate towards yourself as you are to your baby and your family. Give back to yourself and enjoy the progress and the changes you have made. The following chapter will focus on problem-solving some issues that still may be sticking points for a few parents.

Chapter 10

Problem-solving sleep setbacks

Did you know: British researchers in 1996 found that the best nap was a short one taken just after consuming caffeine?

YOU'VE IMPLEMENTED YOUR PLAN AND YOU HAVE SEEN changes, well done. You may be feeling a little exhausted and may have noticed that your baby's sleeping has improved but yours hasn't? Don't be disheartened, the light is nearer than you realise. For you, sleep is just around the corner and you are in the maintenance phase; this is the stage where you keep on doing what you have been doing in order for long-lasting change.

Some of you have done really well on your sleep plan and your baby's sleep has improved but there may be a few minor niggles that are troubling you. Let me address them here for you, so that you too can enter into the maintenance phase of your gentle sleep solution plan.

Dummy dilemmas

The problem with dummies centres on three main themes:

* to use or not to use
* how to use
* when to lose and how to lose

Dummy use is a potent soothing tool as your baby is calmed by their sucking. This aids sleep and research has shown that it can prevent SIDS. Dummy use in my view is a personal choice. In my opinion, dummies can be very helpful and if used correctly can be an effective sleep association, prop and calmer. My own children did not have dummies, instead they chose to suck their hands and their tongues. You can't get rid of hands or tongues and so it is much easier to get rid of or stop using a dummy.

You may decide to avoid this whole particular battle by choosing not to use a dummy with your child. But for those of you who are part of the 'to use' crew then here are some helpful considerations.

By using the dummy functionally you don't fall into the trap of the dummy being a prop that hinders your progress. Parents only use the dummy for sleep in the day and night, to be used to calm baby, and the dummy should be taken out of the baby's mouth if he is crying. Place the dummy in the eyeline of your baby to help him focus and placed back in once the baby is distracted and focused on the dummy in order to calm him. This makes the dummy more powerful and useful in calming.

You can help your baby learn to root for the dummy when he wakes; this can be achieved by instead of you placing the dummy in his mouth, nudge his hands near it so he automatically grabs for the dummy, or place the dummy in your baby's hand and guide his hands towards his mouth if he is unable to put the dummy in his mouth initially. This way you are teaching your baby to administer the soothing tool himself. (self-soothing in action).

In line with the gentle sleep system approach you can begin to gradually limit the use of the dummy at naptime sleeps first, and teach your baby to settle and soothe by replacing it with other functional tools, such as distraction, thumb-sucking or having a comforter. All these are independent of you and do not create a dependency on your presence. A perfect time to do this is when your baby's sucking reflex reduces at three months, although you can still get rid of the dummy when your baby is older.

In terms of how to 'lose' the dummy, for older children you may be able to enlist the help of the 'dummy fairy' who takes all used dummies and sends them to new babies who need them more, replacing the dummy with a small gift. This explanation and involvement with your child will help him know what is going on and what will happen. Smaller children will still be able to understand this concept if you use non-verbal cues, wrapping the dummies up, taking in a pretty box and delivery to the post box or offering it to a friend who may recently have had a baby. Through your behaviour and actions your little one, who may not understand the concept of the fairy, will still understand the process and accept this if done in a way that involves them too.

Whatever you take away from your child, replace with something that is equally rewarding. This could include a new book, a trip out, extra cuddles or any other creative idea that you know he would like. The important point here is to always signpost, always explain what is happening to your child and find a suitable replacement to avoid battles.

No matter the age and stage of development your child is at you can use the gentle sleep system to prepare your child for change. Whether it's how to use the dummy functionally or whether you are taking the dummy away permanently, guide them through change and maintain the changes by using verbal and non-verbal ways of communicating. Remember, you shape your baby's behaviour by adapting the way you respond: taking on a relaxed and mindful approach to the dummy will encourage more of the behaviour you want. All these are key elements within the system and you are using your confidence and your knowledge of your child's temperament to know just the right sets of tools and responses that will work.

Early waking woes

Waking early or at a set time is a key sign of your little one's sleep cycle being set and them thinking that this is an acceptable time to rise and greet the whole family. We on the other hand have other ideas and plans, like sleeping in just a little while longer and encouraging our babies to sleep past 5am. It is possible to reset your baby's body clock, and it is possible for your baby to be restful and even sleep for an hour or so longer, but please bear in mind that it's natural for your baby who is under two to wake for a feed or nappy change around the 5am mark. So, in accordance with the gentle sleep system, we must meet the child's needs first; we do it swiftly and remaining as slow and as calm as possible with as little interaction as possible. Our mood, manner and movement should be calm, consistent and considered. The aim here is to be able to calm your baby so that you will be able to leave the room again and for your baby to either rest or drift off back to sleep.

In the early morning our baby's temperature has dropped and therefore he may feel cold at this time. It's important to remember that we often cuddle our babies with our warm bodies. This has a powerful knock-out effect and if we take them into our beds then this association may become fixed. So rather than develop new unhelpful associations we can use this knowledge of warmth to help our baby to settle back into their bed. Use a wheat bag warmer to warm their space and then remove it once it has done its job. Placing a warm touch on their chest and tucking them in also ensures they are warm and snug.

Our focus at this time should be less on trying to get them back to sleep and more on helping them to feel comfortable, calm and safe. It's okay if he is in the drowsy - awake stage of consciousness at this time. Our behaviour when he wakes early will be key in helping to set or reset his body clock and new expectation. For example, if you always open the curtains at this time, the action of doing so, the light from the window and the sounds you make are all types of communication that send a message to your baby's body clock that it's time to wake, and over time his body rhythm will expect these conditions. The aim, as I have mentioned, is not to focus on getting them back to sleep but making sure our actions and way of communication is sending a message of calm and non-wakefulness. Once our babies are happy to relax and rest in their space we can allow them to do the rest, and if falling back to sleep happens, it happens naturally. If your baby is happy to be gurgling away in her bed and gently minding her own business then that's okay too. I managed to get my twin girls to stay in their cot for an extra hour after they first woke in the morning and I did this by placing their cots so they faced each other and used levels of responsiveness when they were distressed. I gradually left them for longer and longer periods before I went in to greet them. This allowed me time as a single parent to get my other older daughters up and ready for the day ahead.

To increase time in their space use distraction and delay and increase over time in 10-minute increments. You can use rewarding cues to help you (books, milk or clock signals). Remember you are rewarding the calm behaviour as this is what you want to increase and see more of. You should first wait to see if your baby will settle herself – five minutes should suffice, then enter the room and use verbal reassurance and proximity, if needed, to calm. You should then introduce the distraction, which you know your child responds well to. This may be music, comforter or a drink of milk. Once given you should then leave the room and return after 10 minutes. Each day you should increase the time you leave the room for until you are at your desired time.

For younger babies (0–12 months) you may like to stay with them in the room, lying down and mirroring the behaviour you want (this means lying down and showing them what sleep and relaxation look like).

So here are the headlines for managing early wakes:

* Do not start your day at 5am.
* Be calm and remember to PAUSE.
* Meet his needs first (hungry, cold, scared, nappy change).
* He may just want to see you and this is fine as your job is to offer reassurance. Do not engage if you do not need to; remember you are using the levels of distress here.
* Match the level of responsiveness to the level of distress.
* Pick a time you wish to start your day and stick to it (I say between 6–7am is a realistic expectation).
* Your first aim is to get your child happy to be in their space.
* Once he is happy to stay in a calm drowsy state or quiet awake state in bed, he will find it easier to go back to sleep as long as there are no other stimulants or cues present.
* Try not to engage with them verbally.
* Use touch or deep breathing.
* For toddlers, use firm instructions and closed options; these are choices that are limited to only two items. (The blue dress or the red shorts, for example.)
* Start by leaving them for 5–10 minutes and gradually increase this time over several days.
* Play an audio tape of a story or your recorded voice.
* Keep them warm and reassured.

* Place a picture of you and your family in their line of vision.
* Reduce their naps during the day by 15 minutes if they are sleeping longer than 50 minutes.
* Put them to bed earlier by 15–30 minutes for one week. More sleep promotes sleep.
* Use a positive reward system, like buttons, each day he stays in bed longer. You can purchase baby-friendly large wooden buttons or discs that are the size of a small teacup saucer.

Breast and bottle battles

One concern many parents have is how to ensure their baby doesn't fall asleep on the breast or bottle and how to ensure that it does not become a dependency. In situations like these you should try split-feeding at night, and changing the times when you offer the last feed so that it is not so close to falling asleep, but is still a nice cue and association and gets your baby in the right mood. I call this 'milk bliss'. Try giving your baby a short feed before the bath and then the rest of the feed after the bath and before you dress him fully. This will mean your baby is not falling asleep on the breast or bottle and you give him at least ten minutes of awake time where he can learn to fall asleep independently.

Another battle may be that your baby won't take the bottle. Usually when the parents I work with explain this problem to me they mean that their baby prefers the breast and will only take a few sips from the bottle and play around with it. Babies can take a while to get used to things. In evolutionary terms this serves to help us be wary of new things, especially new things we have to put in our mouths and eat. It can take some children up to 26 presentations of the same object or item before they accept it. As parents we see our child turn his head or refuse something and think that he is rejecting it, that he doesn't like it, when all it is is your child being cautious and following his natural instinct. In this situation you will want to habituate your child to the bottle. Try to place less focus on how much milk he drinks as this is less important. When he is comfortable with the bottle he will drink more. The fact that he drinks a little is a good sign. Just like we did with the transitional object we want to have the bottle in sight and in view all the time, not just at feeding time. Place the bottle around the home, get your baby used to seeing it, touching it, playing with it and sucking on it. When you have spent at least three days getting your baby used to having the bottle in their world you should try to get another person at first to offer the feed in the bottle and this should be done over the next three days until feeding from the bottle is established – that means at least one feed in the day is taken with the bottle. Ideally you should be in another part of the home or out if that is possible.

If you are a single parent or you don't have anyone to help feed at the time, try to mask the smell of your milk by wearing a family member's top (it smells of them not you) and feed your baby the bottle at the same time each day once a day for the next three days.

In my experience a large majority of babies do not accept milk from a beaker, although they will drink water from it. This has amazed me and my parents; I have no answers for why this is the case and perhaps it's just down to a baby preferring their milk from a bottle. So children may experience trouble accepting the bottle if they are breastfed and I don't buy into the idea of nipple/teat confusion: I feel our babies are a lot more sophisticated than we give them credit for. I think they are just very good at communicating to us exactly what their preferences are. It is our job, in my view, to help babies accept a range of different things as part of their growth and development. To provide them with what they need, not want they want.

Dealing with distress

It's hard having a baby, it's even harder when you are exhausted and sleep-deprived, and sometimes we don't have or are not allowed to express this frustration and our own distress. It's okay to cry and have your own tantrum, no one is expecting you to be perfect, get it right the first time or even have all the answers. It may be hard to live up to the expectations you had for yourself and the expectations of others and sometimes it feels good to have a good cry. It's okay to accept and acknowledge that what you are going through is tough. It's okay to have your down moments and shut out the noise from the outside world and just sit for a moment and have a good old cry. It is right for you to cry, it is right for you to notice how you feel and it is right to let it out, because if you don't it will only build and build and build, and who knows who may be on the receiving end when we explode. So have your tantrum, have your cry, and don't you dare feel bad about it.

You are not alone and you will not be the first parent or caregiver to wonder what this is all about and wonder if, when and how things will change. You were born to feel and experience a full range of emotions and therefor it is natural to feel sad and want to have a cry once in a while, or more than once in a while as the case may be. You are wonderful, beautiful you, and if your mood takes a turn for the worse and you find it hard to pull yourself away from the negative feelings, this could be a sign of postnatal low mood. Either way there is help and support from friends, family, sleep consultants, psychologists and therapists, whether you are managing this moment of distress on your own or not. But knowing what to do and who to reach out to will be the difference between staying stuck and continuing to move forward. I have included a self-report measure at the back of this book (see Appendices 4 and 5). This is a patient health questionnaire and an anxiety scale which will help you decide if you should visit your GP if your mood has been significantly low for over a week or your anxiety particularly high.

Crying is and will always be one way our babies communicate. Crying is a sign that you too have needs and you require these needs to be met whether it's by you or someone else. Crying means you have something to say, so I say, say it. Accept that this is a natural response and let it out. Once it's out, wipe your eyes, wash your face, turn the page and start again. And this too is okay – ride that wave and allow your emotions to rise and fall.

Chapter 11

Sleep and Special Families

Did you know: The higher your IQ the more sleep-deprived you are?

I HAVE BEEN ASKED TO WORK WITH A WIDE RANGE OF FAMILIES throughout my career as a sleep consultant and one of the most rewarding experiences is helping special families – those with twins or multiples, single parents, and those who are living with children with long-term health conditions and disabilities – gain a few hours' extra sleep and establish a routine and sleep habit appropriate for their baby. My gentle sleep system will work with all families because it involves building your own new unique plan that suits your need for each member of the family. The considerations for those living with disabilities and long-term health conditions and unique make-ups are slightly different and so I feel it's important to mention the slight nuances here.

Having a structured routine is not something I advocate in an explicit way as I believe in following your baby's cues and temperament. However, when it comes to special families, including those with twins and multiples, I give a slightly different 'what works' approach. In these family situations it is probably more helpful to you and your child to have and maintain a structured and well-planned routine that *does* involve doing things at the same time and ideally in the same place where possible. My approach is doing things sequentially, signposting, by developing a routine that is based on cues you are communicating, and that behaviour should correspond with the cue; this is how we form associations through learning what to do when we see, do or hear or are exposed to a set of conditions. For our babies we are gently shaping their behaviour not by rigid routine but by helping them learn how they should act when we respond to them in a certain way. This way of shaping your baby's responses is not only more flexible, causing less stress, but works for nearly all families regardless of composition or lifestyle or special circumstances.

Blended families

Among the many varied families I have worked with over the years, has been the blended family (the stepfamily, the adoptive or foster family). And the numbers are growing. No longer are we tied to the concept of the traditional family, and as we travel nationally and internationally and move further away from our parents and extended family our traditional support systems have been replaced by friends and social networks. As marriages break down and stepfamilies are made, the view of the family has become a multi-coloured beautiful tapestry which has taken on a shape of its own. Your special family needs to know how to navigate the difficulties of sleeping when there may be particular tensions that you would not necessarily see in a traditional family composition, for example, having stepchildren over to stay and dealing with new sleeping arrangements, the change in dynamics and the change in energy within the home, in addition to any discipline issues that may arise from time to time.

This is where the PAUSE method comes into play when managing your emotions, as well as defining roles for each family member to deal with personality issues and keeping people functional and helpful. The gentle sleep system works well with blended families because we are using techniques that involve the whole family and working in a way that promotes inclusiveness and bonding. You may, for example, decide that the biological parent disciplines their children while the step-parent implements the sleep plan. Taking alternate nights and sharing the responsibility helps to take the pressure off. Don't be afraid to ask for help – most people want to help you but are unsure how, so clearly defining each member of the family's role in the bedtime routine will go a long way and then all you need to do is focus on your sleep plan. Give stepchildren a role and job so they feel included in the family home life when they come to stay. Get them to choose a role so that you get a commitment from them or you may like to give them options to choose from such as helping to read stories, be in charge of toy collection (i.e. tidying up). Set aside time for everyone to have fun, get excited and then wind down. You may agree, for example, on those days that it is easier just to have a later bedtime to avoid additional stress for you and give everyone a chance to enjoy each other.

Special babies with disabilities or long-term health conditions (LTC)

You may find that if your baby is born with impairments to her hearing, sight, vision or if she has neurological difficulties, she may differ from those newborns without disabilities. This may mean that when devising a sleep plan, your ear and observations will need to be more acute, it may mean that it takes a little closer looking or a little longer to see, hear and interpret what your baby is communicating to you. You may find that at first you are unsure what your baby may be trying to say to you and how you should respond. Don't let that dissuade you, use the PAUSE method and patiently observe and record any patterns or reflexes associated with body language and sound. Use your thoughts record to build up a visual account of your baby's behaviour and how she has responded to you. Use this information to guide you. You should be mindful of the times and the environment your baby is in when she has been distressed or is expressing a need. The first response is to check that your child's basic needs are being met; these are comfort, discomfort, hunger and boredom needs. Once you have gone through these and your baby remains distressed you should look for signs that she may be overstimulated. We can measure these responses by changes to their state, colouring and movement, such as arching their back or turning their head away from you. Use the body language table here to help you with this (see pages 42–43). Listen out for how your special baby is breathing. You may be able to tell from this if she is unwell or in distress. Knowing this you will be on the right track to soothing her and learning more about her voice and what she is saying to you. For example, you will need to increase the level of touch and smell you provide for a baby who is deaf and blind, due to loss of information from decreased vision and hearing your baby's other senses will be essential for them to be able to be soothed by you and engage in a reciprocal communication. While you are holding your baby close to your chest you should speak so that he can feel the warmth and vibrations from your body. You could also use his hand or foot held close to your mouth and/or chest again to feel the vibrations of your voice. Use consistent touching in a rhythmic and patterned way, and choose a part of the body to demonstrate love and empathy, stroking the head or patting the back. Over time, you can use this as a way to signal and communicate with your child to let them know how you feel, what is happening and what to expect.

You have my permission to be as creative as you like with your baby when you are trying to soothe them. Ideally you want to make sure you are sticking to the principles of functional behaviour and sending your baby the same consistent message. But the *how* part with your special baby will vary and require a little bit more focus and attention. Try to significantly reduce the stimulation from the environment, this includes light, noise and social stimulants such as people, devices and such. Using household objects and the car for drives around your home area can be very effective at soothing your baby – the sounds of vibration and consistent movement can be very calming for your baby, and the monotonous continuous sound will offer your child an excellent way to ground them to their environment. Remember not to worry about these things becoming unhelpful or a hindrance: props are useful as they can help and aid your sleep plan. Used functionally you can help your special baby to calm so they can focus on the sleeping part.

Over time you will learn what works best for your baby, what sequences, length and conditions are optimal. Don't forget to record these events in your sleep log so that you can build up a view and pattern of your baby's behaviour.

We have talked about responsive parenting and how touch and eye contact are so beneficial to baby calming and getting them in the right state for sleep. The feedback from this type of interaction may be significantly reduced with babies who have visual or auditory impairments. Adapting the position of lights and objects so that your baby may see your face more clearly, may also work best for your child, but by consulting with your specialist you can shape your environment and behaviour so that it works with your baby and their special needs.

By using your smell and a special scent for each family member you can help your baby who may not hear so well keep from being startled, so that she knows when you have entered the room. These types of cueing and signalling can be as creative as you like and work well with all babies, not just the extra-special ones.

Finding ways to touch and care for your baby in a way that she finds pleasurable is a learning objective for parents with special babies, and especially those with motor impairments and seizures. Some babies who suffer from seizure disorders may experience triggers through touch and parents may feel inclined to touch their babies less. Knowing how your child responds to the pressure of your embrace, the sensation of your touch and how you may stroke him and in what direction will improve the quality of your calming and bonding experience and aid sleep.

The benefits of touching, holding and movement can be seen and felt in a baby's physiological and emotional well-being. Lung congestion and gastric function can be improved just by touch. And movement can help with digestion and the absorption of food, so a gentle rocking in a functional fashion can help your baby's body work well. I recommend a dose of baby massage before bedtime as a sure-fire way of aiding your baby's quality of life.

Trips to the hospital

Often hospitalisation can lead to a disruption to the sleeping pattern. Here I can show you how you can carry your sleep plan with you and almost eliminate any problems. Changes to the routine can be compensated for by using your grounding tools – bring with you the items that are attached to the sense and introduce him to the new environment and then use your presence as the reassuring and consolidating element. You see this plan works well if you have a lot of hospital trips because we are controlling all the variables that could possibly cause your child to be unsettled and not sleep. We are bringing with us the things that help your child feel safe and comforted, such as a picture of you, his bed sheets that smell of home and his transitional object.

Twins and multiples

The trick I learnt very quickly with my twins was synchronisation. Synch their routine fast, and start as you mean to go on. The idea here is to be organised and planned and have what you need close to hand. Feed, bathe, dress and sleep your babies at the same time, this is the easiest way to manage twins and more. Even if your babies fall asleep and wake at different times keep them both in synch. You want to avoid the situation of having one awake while the other sleeps as this means your day will be full of giving all your attention to at least one baby 100 per cent of the time. Allow them to share a room and when they wake get them up when they are both awake, allowing them to rise naturally. They will be company to each other – my twins would lie happily chatting for 30–45 minutes in the morning before needing my assistance. When dealing with a crying baby that has woken from a sleep my advice is to fight one fire at a time should the other one wake and become unsettled. Rather than shifting your attention from one to the other, focus on one and have them calmed and feeling happy before you tend to the other child. This plan of action will ensure that you feel in control of the situation and not pulled in competing directions. Remember the PAUSE method and be mindful. In fact, mindfulness with twins and multiples is a very good idea to achieve success.

Single parents

I want to send a special message to single parents because I know this story personally. I have been a single mum for most of my children's lives. I know how hard it can be at times and how it can feel as though you can't go on and that things will never change. More importantly I understand the emotions you feel when you look at your situation and challenge the unfairness of it. Some single parents may be celebrating because raising their baby on their own has been a conscious choice. But my message is simple no matter how you came to be a single parent.

When I looked round my social group all my friends were married, some happily and others not so happily. When I looked at them, I initially looked through with glasses that were negative and this made me feel bad. Then one day – I remember it clearly – I was bathing my twin girls who were 14 months old at the time. I realised that I was very fortunate to be the one who puts my kids to bed and shares these tender moments, laughing and staring into their eyes and falling in love with them all over again each and every day. I saw that I was indeed very lucky in my situation and that so many other people may also think I was lucky – I had two little helpers aged 11 and 6 and they loved supporting me and helping to take care of their little sisters. I had twins who had helped to shape me into a more organised and structured person. I looked at myself and realised that I had changed my glasses and my view on the world; my situation as a result was a more helpful one. I realised that I could rely on me, I realised that I did not have to expect anything from anyone else and feel let down when my expectations were not met. I began to realise how strong and resilient I was. I began, for the first time, to notice my strengths as a mother.

So my message to all single parents is to never forget to look at your situation with the right glasses on – the glasses that help you feel better about your situation and make the most of it, the glasses that will help you put your plan into action and guide you towards success. Your situation is unique and where you have strengths these may be other people's weaknesses, so celebrate and be happy for all your amazing strengths that will get you through helping your child to sleep on your own. You will tailor this plan by giving yourself the roles and being clear about what role you will play and when; you will be in such an amazing position to be consistent as you are the only one putting your baby to sleep.

Remember that however your family is made up, you are unique and so is your family. Your special situation has many inherent challenges but also many wonderful qualities and affords you wonderful opportunities you may never have experienced. Your journey on the plan may be bumpier than other families. But I want you to draw strength from the fact that you can help your baby sleep naturally. That every opportunity you face makes you learn and you will learn harder and faster than most because your road is a steep one, but with your huge learning curve in life you will surely, for all your sterling effort, receive the greatest of all rewards.

Conclusion

Adapting Your Plan According to Your Child's Needs

YOU WANT TO GET TO THE END OF YOUR SLEEP PLAN AND know that you have reached your goal, so I advise that in order to do this we need you to stay on top of things. Use your sleep diary as a bridge – use the information from your log and change your responses according to your child's progress, mood and sleeping style. This will mean you are adapting with your child.

There is a tendency that when we find something that works we stick to it, even when our child is no longer responding. I don't want this for you; I want you to know why things work and why things don't. I don't want you to become wedded to the idea that it is the 'tool' that works, for example, the dummy or the bedtime routine. I want you to be your own sleep consultant and know that it is the model that works not the specific tool. As our children develop their needs will change, and so your response has to match that, but never lose sight of how you meet their needs: always using PAUSE, levels of responsiveness and bonding tools. As your baby gets older they may no longer want to hear white noise but prefer a song or a story. As your child gets older, sticker charts may no longer be effective but praise and rewarding activities are. The principle remains the same: you are adapting and changing to your child's stage of development. Your child may become ill and you need to go back to holding them and giving them milk or water in the night. Don't fear that this is a step back but rather move up and down the steps of your plan. We are confident we can get back on the right track because we are always and will always be sending our children the same message – 'I will meet your need and you will fall asleep independently. I will leave pieces of me behind, you won't feel alone. I will teach you to trust me and I will always return.'

Each week you should analyse your sleep log. Often things feels worse than they are and this will help to motivate you, also you will be able to see what you need to change and what you need to keep doing. Compare your weeks, use your previous weeks to see how you have progressed and measure your change. At the end of your programme you should have at least five weeks of sleep logs. This is your opportunity to make any tweaks, changes or adaptations to your plan. This is all part of the monitoring and maintenance of your plan to keep you on the road to success.

Avoid sleep traps

The first trap to avoid is rescuing the other partner. Going in when you hear the other parent trying to settle the baby can keep the sleep problem going for two main reasons: firstly, it creates a more wakeful state as baby has two dance parents instead of one, and secondly it undermines the other parent's ability to calm baby, thereby robbing them of the opportunity to feel confident. Rescuing the other parent may seem like the humane thing to do but it doesn't help you or your sleep plan. Allow the other parent to practise, learn and figure out their own dance steps as their own experience builds their confidence.

The second trap to avoid is giving up. Working on a gentle sleep plan takes time, effort and dedication – you are learning all the time and you are also in the dual role as teacher, shaping your baby's behaviour as well as your own. So it makes sense that you may have thought about giving up. When you have been in your baby's room for an hour and you are thinking that things will never change and you might as well give up, this is the time to stay. By giving up you will undo all the hard work you have done so far, by giving up you are going back two or three stages in your plan and it will be an even steeper hill to climb once you have gone back, and your willpower will have lessened. Don't give up. Don't give up because our babies or children only learn by the change in outcome. The process may be hard for us as parents and the gentle sleep system will take two or three weeks to achieve, but our children are not bothered by the process, the time and space in between where we are and where we want to be. They do not see the effort we are making. Babies only learn by the last thing we did before they went to sleep. So while giving up may seem attractive, it will keep your problem going because your baby will hold out for that very last thing that you did. Stay focused, stay on track and don't give up.

We have a tendency to focus on time and the process as this is what is important to us. However, this is not what changes behaviour – instead the last thing we did when our babies fell asleep changes expectations and behaviour. So if you have been used to rocking your baby to sleep and you try a different dance, like putting him in his cot instead of rocking, and it takes 30 minutes, you might think of giving up as in your view it's taking too long. If you go back to rocking and your baby falls asleep, your baby will learn that rocking works and the next night he will take an hour to go to sleep in his cot as he is holding out for the rocking. Say instead you had your baby in the cot and calmed him for 40 minutes and stuck at it, rocked him within the cot gently and only when he cried, and 45 minutes later he fell asleep in the cot without being rocked, the learning is that he can sleep on his own. The next night he will remember this and it may take only 20 minutes to settle him and for him to fall asleep, and over time this new learning will reduce the time it takes to settle and there you have it – your baby's body rhythm is joined up and he is sleeping well.

The final trap to avoid is giving in to favours. They come in all shapes and guises but they are all the same – when the roles become reversed and our children begin to charm us and we stop charming them. When you notice you are being charmed be forewarned, the inevitable next mistaken step is for us to give in to favours. Our little darlings will try to use their charm to get whatever it is they think they need at the time to either keep you with them, avoid sleep or just continue the fun they have been having.

We can allow our babies to charm us, after all it feels good and it lets us know they love us right back. Just remember these wise words: don't give in! Don't keep putting the dummy back in, don't give the water, the juice, the tenth book, the hundredth cuddle, the endless trips to the bathroom. Whatever ruse our babies may present to us, remember the PAUSE and respond appropriately, functionally and using the levels of responsiveness to send the same consistent message.

Key points

Do:	Don't:
Use verbal reassurance	Give in to favours (water, milk, toys)
Spend time in the day (15 minutes) increasing her time playing in her room	Let her lead
Read two or three stories	Rescue the other parent
Ignore negative behaviour	Pick her up and carry her
Praise positive behaviour	Get into a fight with her
Keep her space warm	
Tuck her in (should be in bed awake for at least 15 minutes)	Take her out of the bed
Roll with resistance	Offer any favours (water, milk, toys)
Use statements	Give up
Stay with her until she falls asleep	Answer any questions (aged 12 months+
Show her safe, happy images	Ask questions
Leave the room and tell her you will be back shortly	
Return to the room before she calls out or becomes anxious	

Chireal's Tip Bits

Charm the charming, take the lead and let your baby follow you.

In summary, we have talked about the importance of attachment and bonding tools that will aid our babies' sleep. We have looked at the underlying reasons why our children won't sleep and we have discussed how you go about applying those techniques, how you respond to your child when she is going to bed and when she is waking. You understand that sometimes your own thoughts and feelings about the problem you are experiencing can make it worse and become a barrier that keeps your problem going. We have discovered that there are three main reasons (anxiety, dependency, sleep cycle) why your baby's sleeping habit may not be where you would like it to be. Importantly, we now know that there are many ways in which we can change behaviour, but that CBT, mindfulness and attachment theory are evidence-based models that have been shown to be effective in changing behaviour.

We don't know what the consequences are yet to some sleep-training methods, but what we can confidently say with the gentle sleep system is that our children will not feel abandoned, they will become more resilient to stress, we will limit and minimise their distress and they will learn and continue to learn. This is a progressive sleep plan that changes behaviour through understanding the needs of the family. Rather than taking away it gives, it replaces, it teaches and this is why it works. It works for the reasons that our children know what to expect from us, we know how to read their behaviour and we know how to respond to them without creating dependencies that are not sustainable.

You have put the model of the gentle sleep plan together and have worked hard over the last four weeks on taking your whole family through a journey of change. You didn't simply just take up the chapter on bonding tools and start implementing these without thought, you were considered, you were mindful and you PAUSEd. You took the time out to really pick the sense from the nonsense and challenge your views and your old ways of thinking. You used all the golden keys that were offered to you and you unlocked the door to your child's healthy sleeping habit. This change, while it may have taken four to six weeks to achieve, will be long-lasting, through all the developmental stages, through illness and through travel, and as life carries on. I admire your hard work, well done.

Chireal's blueprint for sleeping success

* PAUSE: this tool will enable you to understand the behaviour patterns within your family.
* Acknowledge family systems: the emphasis is on the family informing behaviour through their communication and understanding. The child is not the focus of the problem.
* Develop trust/be present: when your child cries be there to understand what she needs, comfort and offer reassurance.
* Increase confidence/slow down your reactions, preparation and household life: remember bedtime should be on a continuum (a seamless transition from being awake to being asleep) leading to and ending in sleep. All your actions and responses should be in line with this process.
* Observe and learn your child's behaviour/language: your child is the only manual you need.
* Communication: talk to your child, explain what is happening, why it is happening, what is going to happen next. This reduces conflict, stress and tears.
* Firm boundaries are like a big cuddle; they represent safety, love and reassurance.

Golden Keys

Cues, props and associations that are independent of the parent.

The sounds, smells and touch your baby loves.

How you feel, what you feel, how intensely you feel it, and how your emotions change and what you do when you actively respond to your child can shape and influence your baby's behaviour.

Open your eyes to your everyday successes – there are many and you are doing really well.

Match your level of intervention to your child's level of distress.

Your smell will help your baby become attached to the object that you leave behind with him or her.

When leaving your child, return to the room before he or she gets anxious and always tell your child that he or she is safe and you will return. For babies who have not acquired language, this can be done through your body language and repetitive behaviour.

When measuring your baby's sleep, think in terms of both 'macro' changes – big changes – and 'micro' changes – the small changes that can add up to big changes. Acknowledging micro-changes will help you remain focused and keep your eyes on the end goal.

Work out what your roadblocks are to establishing good sleeping patterns, and devise ways in which to overcome them.

You are the master golden key, you are the expert on your baby and you either already know what your baby needs, or can easily acquire the skills necessary for good sleep patterns. You are doing really well.

Example of a Sleep Diary

Pre-plan

NAME.SB Client Boy

WEEK pre plan	Date/Day of week						
WHO PUT HIM IN BED	**FRIDAY** Mum	**SATURDAY** Mum	**SUNDAY** Mum	**MONDAY** Mum	**TUESDAY** Mum	**WEDNESDAY** Mum	**THURSDAY** Mum
Time woke in morning	7:50	7:00	6:50	7:15	6:50	7:35	7:00
Time and length of nap(s) in day	10:00–10:30 on my lap while I was on the phone! 2:30–3:30 in his cot	12:30–1:20 in his bed	12:25–1:15 in bed 5:25–5:55 in car	12:00–12:50 at nursery	12:20–12:55 in nursery	12–12:30 in nursery	2:30–3:30 after refusing naps from 12:30 onwards. Fell asleep on me
Time start prep. for bed in evening	5:50 bath	6:15 bath	6:20	6:10 bath	5:50 bath	6:15 play upstairs	Bath 6:00 but then got distracted by cousin arriving for us to babysit
Time went to bed in evening	6:30	6:45	6:40	6:35	6:30	6:40	7:20

Time went to sleep	6:45	7:00 seems happy to go to bed with bottle	7:40! Clearly not tired enough due to late nap. But didn't cry too much. Two more squeals/cries within next 10 mins	6:40 – really wants his bottle! Asleep in 5 mins … obviously tired! But he wasn't grumpy beforehand	6:45 no milk in bed. 15 mins of throwing toys and himself and complaining	6:55 15 mins drama	7:25 good bedtime, drank all his milk on my lap sleepily, then sleeping bag and brushing teeth, cried hard but only briefly, asleep in 5 mins
Woke up	7:20–7:40 11:30–11:45 5:30–5:45 6:30 cried	9:45–10 stood crying but lay down when asked, grabbed his bottle, sucked even after empty 12–12:15 Dad went 4–4:45 way too awake!	10:40–10:45 milk, howling again 5 mins after I left him, 10 more mins to settle 1:50–2:00 4:45–5:20	7:30–7:35 10:15–10:20 12:15–12:55 3–?? I fell asleep 4:25–?? Dad fell asleep 6:00 Dad still there	7:25–7:30 settled himself, and about 3 more times 10:20-midnight crying 4:20–5:25 unsettled 6:20–6:35 took upstairs	7:30–7:45 9:20–9:40 11:30-settled himself 00:40–01:10 1:20–1:50 4:50–6:30	8:50–8:55 1:00–01:15 3–??? Dad fell asleep there until 5 5:40 spent an hour in his room, then took upstairs but would not go back to sleep
What you did	Tried to not give my hand to hold		Stands in bed crying each time again. But calms down relatively quickly when I come and pat bed. Sometimes he reaches for me		At 10:40 looked like he was asleep, but as soon as I got to bed he started again, Gave in and gave milk, changed nappy… did not settle, kept lying down but then getting up and crying again	Nappy change around 5:10, milk around 5:30, drank most of it, took upstairs at 6, slept a little bit between 6:30 and 7	Gave milk at 6am – again he drank the whole lot (not in one go)

WEEK pre plan	Date/Day of Week						
WHO PUT HIM IN BED	FRIDAY Mum	SATURDAY Mum	SUNDAY Mum	MONDAY Mum	TUESDAY Mum	WEDNESDAY Mum	THURSDAY Mum
Time(s) went to sleep again		At 4 took ages for him to fall asleep. Eventually he lies quietly on his side and breathes as if asleep but with eyes open, or keeps opening them. If I leave – huge protest	Same as yester-day at 4:45		Roughly the same story at 4:30, though without milk or nappy change Gave new milk at 6:30, he drank quite a bit and then slept for another hour		
Comments			He's back to waking at least 3 times a night … argh!		Chireal chat in afternoon. Only had about 60ml of milk between dinner and going to bed	Waking up 6 times a night and not settling … it's GOT TO STOP!!!	

Week 1

NAME.Client SB Boy

WEEK 1	Date/Day of Week						
WHO PUT HIM IN BED	**FRIDAY Mum**	**SATURDAY Dad**	**SUNDAY Dad**	**MONDAY Mum**	**TUESDAY Dad**	**WEDNESDAY Mum**	**THURSDAY dad**
Time woke in morning	7:00	7? 8? 9:30? Hard to say because we stayed in bed	7:35	7:40 he sat up in his bed, checked his empty bottle, didn't cry	7:00	7:40	6:50
Time & length of nap(s) in day	9:45–10:10 4:50–5:30	Slept on and off on me during the morning/early afternoon,	1:30–2pm only, after fighting in his bed for an hour earlier (11–12). Slept in his bed and woke up and played!	10:30–11:00 after 20mins protest in his bed 1:50–2:10 in car	11:00–12:15 at nursery 4:00–4:15 in car	10:55–11:40 at nursery	10:30–10:50 in his bed, woke up coughing 2:30–2:40 in his bed, then coughing fit and vomited all over his bed
Time start prep. for bed in evening	6:10 bath, was quite moany	7:15, no bath	6:20 (but had bath before dinner)	6:50 no bath (late due to saying good bye to grand parents)	6:50	6:10 bath	No bath
Time went to bed in evening	6:30 quite a bit of fuss	7:30, took ages to settle. Kept falling asleep but waking 5mins later	6:30?	7:00	6:50ish settle in travel cot	6:35	Bed at 6 so tired as no proper afternoon sleep

WEEK 1	Date/Day of Week						
WHO PUT HIM IN BED	FRIDAY Mum	SATURDAY Dad	SUNDAY Dad	MONDAY Mum	TUESDAY Dad	WEDNESDAY Mum	THURSDAY dad
Time went to sleep	6:50	8:30??	6:35? he only took 5 mins	7:05	7:30ish in her arms	6:40	
Woke up	7.30–7.50 8.30–8.45 5.30–6.30	9.50–10.00	8:30–8.40 4:45 am	4:30 cried a little but went back to sleep 6:20 majorly upset, didn't settle, in and out of quiet 6:40 up again	Transferred to car around 10:15pm, was awake during car journey, asleep in his own cot around 10:45 5:10–5:40	Woke 4.50	4:55–5:10
What you did	Lots of touching, rocking and verbal reassurance	Settled him with touch and a bit of rocking functionally in his bed mostly.	Both times in the night he cried but went back to sleep on his own	Verbal reassurance	At 5:10 gave him milk as wanted him to go back to sleep…	Waited to see if he would settle himself	Waited , listened to coughing but he feel back to sleep on his own
Time(s) went to sleep again	Slept ok ish until between 9 and 5.30					5am	5.10
Comments	But work at 5.30 and didn't want to go back to sleep, got up at 7am	Best night ever					

Week 2

NAME.Client SB boy 15 mths

WEEK 2	Date/Day of Week						
Who Put Him In Bed	**FRIDAY Dad**	**SATURDAY Dad**	**SUNDAY Dad**	**MONDAY Mum**	**TUESDAY Mum**	**WEDNESDAY Mum**	**THURSDAY Mum**
Time woke in morning	7.30	7.00	5:30	6:30	7,00	7.00	7:10
Time & length of nap(s) in day	10.–1.30 2.30–3.30	10.–10.45 2.00–3.10	9:45–10:30 on my bed with me 1.30–2.30	10–11 1.45–2.45	10–11:30 in buggy on walk 1.45–2.30	On and off all afternoon… miserable again	10.–11 1.30–2.30
Time start prep. for bed in evening	5.30 bath	6.30pm	5.30	5.30	6	5.30	5.30
Time went to bed in evening	6.30	7pm, didn't give milk, he didn't want any anyway, just a few sips water	6.30	6:30 Absolutely knackered, fell asleep immediately	6:40	6:15	6:25
Time went to sleep	6.45	7.10	6.45	6:30	6:45 happy	6:35	6:30

WEEK 2	Date/Day of Week						
Who Put Him In Bed	FRIDAY Dad	SATURDAY Dad	SUNDAY Dad	MONDAY Mum	TUESDAY Mum	WEDNESDAY Mum	THURSDAY Mum
Woke up	Once but resettled himself	Once but resettled himself	4:30–5:30	4:45	4.30	5:00	5.10
What you did	listened		Gave milk,	Gave milk	verbally reassured at 4.30 wake did not give milk	verbally reassured at 5amwake did not give milk	Waited to see if he would resettle
Time(s) went to sleep again	N/A		5.30	5am	4.45	5.10	5.15
Comments	Slept through to 5am, then squeaked once in a while	Slept until 5 and was awake talking not really sure what to do here			Chat with Chireal		Prob struggled with blocked nose

Appendix 2

Blank Sleep Diary

WEEK	Date/Day of Week						
WHO PUT BABY IN BED	FRIDAY	SATURDAY	SUNDAY	MONDAY	TUESDAY	WEDNESDAY	THURSDAY
Time woke in morning							
Time & length of nap(s) in day							
Time start prep. for bed in evening							
Time went to bed in evening							
Time went to sleep							
Woke up							
What you did							
Time(s) went to sleep again							
Comments							

Appendix 3

Blank Thoughts Record

Situation	Automatic unhelpful thought	Emotions	Balanced helpful thought	Emotions with balanced thought

Appendix 4

Anxiety Scale

GAD-7				
Over the <u>last 2 weeks</u>, how often have you been bothered by the following problems? *(Use "✓" to indicate your answer)*	**Not at all**	**Several days**	**More than half the days**	**Nearly every day**
1. Feeling nervous, anxious or on edge	0	1	2	3
2. Not being able to stop or control worrying	0	1	2	3
3. Worrying too much about different things	0	1	2	3
4. Trouble relaxing	0	1	2	3
5. Being so restless that it is hard to sit still	0	1	2	3
6. Becoming easily annoyed or irritable	0	1	2	3
7. Feeling afraid as if something awful might happen	0	1	2	3
(For office coding: Total Score T ______ = ______ + ______ + ______)				

Developed by Drs. Robert L. Spitzer, Janet B.W. Williams, Kurt Kroenke and colleagues, with an educational grant from Pfizer Inc. No permission required to reproduce, translate, display or distribute.

Appendix 5

Patient Questionnaire

PATIENT HEALTH QUESTIONNAIRE - 9 (PHQ - 9)				
Over the <u>last 2 weeks</u>, how often have you been bothered by any of the following problems? *(Use "✓" to indicate your answer)*	**Not at all**	**Several days**	**More than half the days**	**Nearly every day**
1. Little interest or pleasure in doing things	0	1	2	3
2. Feeling down, depressed, or hopeless	0	1	2	3
3. Trouble falling or staying asleep, or sleeping too much	0	1	2	3
4. Feeling tired or having little energy	0	1	2	3
5. Poor appetite or overeating	0	1	2	3
6. Feeling bad about yourself — or that you are a failure or have let yourself or your family down	0	1	2	3
7. Trouble concentrating on things, such as reading the newspaper or watching television	0	1	2	3
8. Moving or speaking so slowly that other people could have noticed? Or the opposite — being so fidgety or restless that you have been moving around a lot more than usual	0	1	2	3
9. Thoughts that you would be better off dead or of hurting yourself in some way	0	1	2	3

FOR OFFICE CODING ___0___ + ______ + ______ + ______
= Total Score: ______

If you checked off <u>any</u> problems, how <u>difficult</u> have these problems made it for you to do your work, take care of things at home, or get along with other people?

Not difficult at all	Somewhat difficult	Very difficult	Extremely difficult
☐	☐	☐	☐

Developed by Drs. Robert L. Spitzer, Janet B.W. Williams, Kurt Kroenke and colleagues, with an educational grant from Pfizer Inc. No permission required to reproduce, translate, display or distribute.

Appendix 6

Sleep Quiz

Sleep quiz: the Chireal sleep measure

This short quiz will help you identify the underlying reason your child is not sleeping. We can then use your answers to build a plan that is unique to your child's temperament and the roles you are playing in your family to help your child gain a healthy sleeping habit.

Note: This quiz is designed to provide you with a quick and easy assessment of your child's sleeping issue. By completing the questions below you will discover what your child's main underlying sleep problem is. This will allow you to effectively target the real reasons your child is not sleeping, meaning greater success.

Dependency	Not at all	Only occasionally	Sometimes	Most of the time
My baby will only go to sleep sucking/rocking/ being held	0	1	2	3
My baby wakes frequently and at different times throughout the night and day	0	1	2	3
My baby has always had problems falling asleep and/or staying asleep	0	1	2	3
My baby needs specific objects present in order to sleep	0	1	2	3

Sleep Quiz

	No Issue/Mild	Mild/Moderate	Moderate/Severe
Answers	0–4	5–8	9–12

Anxiety	Not at all	Only occasionally	Sometimes	Most of the time
My baby is distressed whenever I leave the room	0	1	2	3
My baby needs to hold my hand/hair in order to fall sleep	0	1	2	3
My baby is clingy during the day and night	0	1	2	3
My baby prefers one parent to settle to sleep and give comfort	0	1	2	3

	No Issue/Mild	Mild/Moderate	Moderate/Severe
Answers	0–4	5–8	9–12

Sleep Cycle	Not at all	Only occasionally	Sometimes	Most of the time
My baby wakes at roughly the same times each night	0	1	2	3
My baby is an early riser	0	1	2	3
My baby takes a long time to settle at night	0	1	2	3
My baby has had periods of time when she has slept well	0	1	2	3

	No Issue/Mild	Mild/Moderate	Moderate/Severe
Answers	0–4	5–8	9–12

Your results	Score	Severity
Dependency		
Anxiety		
Sleep Cycle		

Appendix 7

CBT Sleep Formulation

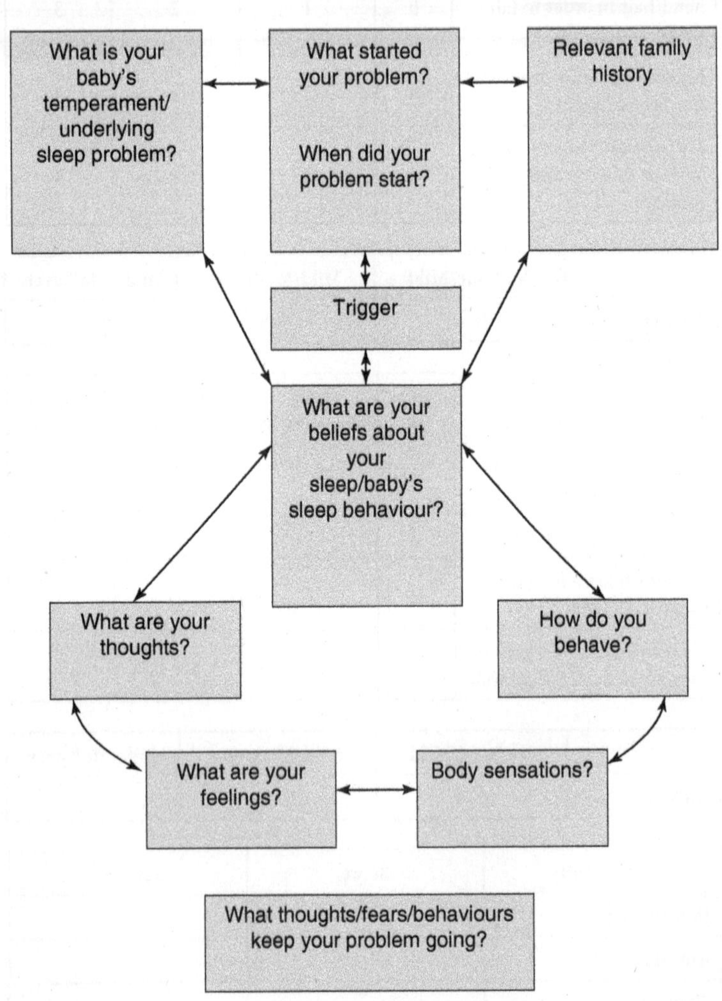

CBT Sleep Formulation

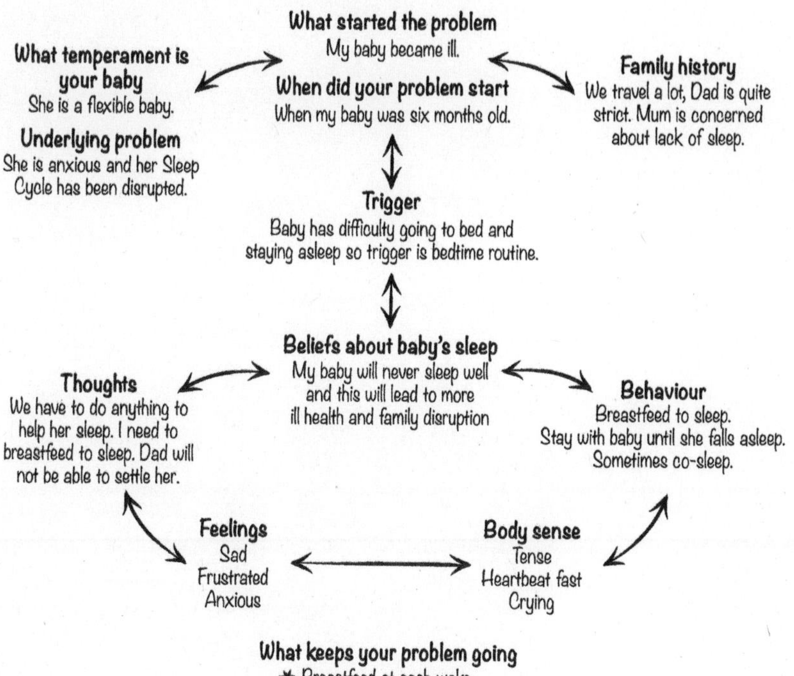

What started the problem
My baby became ill.
When did your problem start
When my baby was six months old.
What temperament is your baby
She is a flexible baby.
Underlying problem
She is anxious and her Sleep Cycle has been disrupted.
Family history
We travel a lot, Dad is quite strict. Mum is concerned about lack of sleep.
Trigger
Baby has difficulty going to bed and staying asleep so trigger is bedtime routine.
Beliefs about baby's sleep
My baby will never sleep well and this will lead to more ill health and family disruption
Thoughts
We have to do anything to help her sleep. I need to breastfeed to sleep. Dad will not be able to settle her.
Behaviour
Breastfeed to sleep.
Stay with baby until she falls asleep.
Sometimes co-sleep.
Feelings
Sad
Frustrated
Anxious
Body sense
Tense
Heartbeat fast
Crying

What keeps your problem going

- Breastfeed at each wake.
- Stay all night with baby.

Resources

Sleep Consultancy (for parents)
Naturally Nurturing Children's Sleep and Behaviour Clinic
www.babysleepclinic.co.uk
info@babysleepclinic.co.uk
0844 826 5458

Sleep Consultant Training (for professionals)
Naturally Nurturing Children's Sleep and Behaviour Clinic
www.babysleepclinic.co.uk
Chireal@babysleepclinic.co.uk
0844 826 5458

Pregnancy and Birth
http://www.natalhypnotherapy.co.uk
+44 (0) 1252 716859

Parenting
The Science of Parenting by Margot Sunderland

A Clinical Guide to Sleep Disorders in Children and Adolescents by Gregory Stores

Breastfeeding Consultant
http://www.jenfox.co.uk
+44 (0) 7595 465 503

Further reading on CBT and Mindfulness
An Introduction to Cognitive Behaviour Therapy
David Westbrook, Helen Kennerley and Joan Kirk

The Mindful Way Through Depression: Freeing Yourself from Chronic Unhappiness (includes Guided Meditation Practices CD) by Mark Williams

Compassion focused therapy
Paul Gibert
www.compassionatemind.co.uk

Index

Index